Human Rights in the Curriculum

Mathematics

Bringing Citizenship to life in the maths classroom

Acknowledgements

Amnesty International UK would like to thank the following people,
without whose help this book would not have been published:

Firstly, the editor and author Peter Wright and contributing authors
Phil Dodd, Jane Giffould and Marie Nassor.

The teachers and students in trialling schools:
Phil Dodd and students at Houghton Kepier School, Tyneside
Steven Downes and students at City of Portsmouth Girls' School
Becky Edwards, Sue Pullen and students at St. Edward's College, West Derby, Liverpool
Jane Giffould and students at Greenwood Special School, Essex
Marie Nassor and students at Norbury Manor High School, Croydon, London
Hema Soni and students at Lampton School, Middlesex
Peter Wright and students at Crown Woods School, Greenwich, London

For additional specialist help and advice, Shane Comer, Eleri Elliott,
Liz Wharton and Gillian Williams.

And Liz Richards, for letting us reprint extracts from her website
'Everything you always wanted to know about maths (but were afraid to ask)'
at www.liz.richards.btinternet.co.uk/webpage.htm

Amnesty International

Amnesty International is a worldwide, independent, voluntary movement of people working to promote the human rights enshrined in the Universal Declaration of Human Rights, through campaigning, education and pressure on governments to ratify and implement human rights treaties.

It is a democratic, self-governing movement with more than a million members. It is independent of any government, political persuasion or religious creed, and is funded by its membership and by public donations. Its work is based on careful research.

Amnesty International opposes some of the gravest violations by governments of people's civil and political rights. Members work for the release of all prisoners of conscience; for fair and prompt trials for all political prisoners; for the abolition of the death penalty, torture and other ill-treatment of prisoners; for an end to political killings and 'disappearances'. Amnesty calls on armed political groups to respect human rights and to halt abuses such as hostage taking, torture and unlawful killings.

Amnesty International campaigns for human rights through its work with the United Nations and regional intergovernmental organisations. It also works for refugees, on international military, security and police relations, and on economic and cultural relations.

Youth Action

Amnesty International Youth Action is made up of campaigning groups of young people in more than 600 schools, sixth form colleges and youth organisations across the UK. They work for the aims of Amnesty International, usually under the wing of a teacher or youth leader.

Youth Action groups receive regular information about Amnesty International's campaigns and copies of the organisation's youth magazine *New Release*. Many are involved in writing Urgent Action appeals. Younger pupils can join in the monthly actions of the Junior Urgent Action Network.

For further information or for details of how to set up a group, please contact:

Amnesty International UK,
Youth and Education Office,
99–119 Rosebery Avenue,
London EC1R 4RE.
Tel: 020 7814 6200
Email: student@amnesty.org.uk
Website: www.amnesty.org.uk

Curriculum Links

How the activities in this book link to the mathematics curriculum in England, Wales, Scotland and Northern Ireland

Note: all activities in this book are also relevant to Attainment Target 1: Using and Applying Mathematics (England and Wales) and Processes in Mathematics (Northern Ireland).

Activity	Attainment target and level				
	England	**Wales**	**N.Ireland**	**Scotland**	**UDHR Article**
	Number & calculation	Number & algebra	Number	Number, money & measurement	
1 Yoruba numbers	3 - 5	3 - 5	3 - 5	D - F	27
2 Russian multiplication	4 - 5	4 - 5	3 - 5	E - F	27
3 Election	4 - 6	4 - 6	4	E - F	21
4 Egyptian multiplication	4 - 6	4 - 6	5	E onwards	27
5 Kaprekar constant	4 - 6	4 - 6	5 - 7	D onwards	27
6 Kaprekar numbers	4 - 6	4 - 6	6 - 7	D onwards	27
7 Gerrymander	5 - 7	5 - 7	7	F onwards	21
8 Chinese primes	5 - 7	5 - 7	6 - 7	E, F and credit	27
16 Brahmagupta's problem	4 - 5	4 - 5	6 - 7	E onwards	27
19 Fair trade chocolate	4 - 6	4 - 6	5 - 6	D onwards	23
	Shape & space	Shape, space & measures	Shape & space	Shape, position & movement	
9 Amish quilt design	3 - 5	3 - 5	4 - 6	E, F onwards	18
10 Yantras	3 - 5	3 - 5	3 - 5	D onwards	18
11 Bath water	4 - 5	4 - 5	4 - 6	D - F	3
12 How big is the world?	4 - 5	4 - 5	4 - 6	E onwards	2
13 Bore hole	4 - 6	4 - 6	5	E, F and general or credit	17 & 24
	Games & puzzles/ Using & applying mathematics	Games & puzzles/ Using & applying mathematics	Games & puzzles/ Processes in mathematics	Games & puzzles/ Problem solving	
14 Magic dominoes	3 - 5	3 - 5	3 - 5	C onwards	27
15 Ayo	4 - 5	4 - 5	4 - 5	E onwards	27
16 Brahmugupta's problem	4 - 5	4 - 5	6 - 7	E onwards	27
17 Totolospi	5 - 7	5 - 7	5 - 7	F & credit	27
	Handling data	Handling data	Handling data	Information handling	
18 Life expectancy	3 - 5	3 - 5	4 - 5	C onwards	3 & 25
19 Fair trade chocolate	4 - 6	4 - 6	5 - 6	D onwards	23
20 Gender images	4 - 6	4 - 6	3 - 6	E onwards	1 & 2
21 World literacy	4 - 6	4 - 6	5	E onwards	26 & 28
22 Average wages	5 - 6	5 - 6	5 - 7	F and credit	23
23 Child labour	5 - 6	5 - 6	5 - 6	E onwards	25
24 Duties survey	5 - 6	5 - 6	5 - 6	E onwards	29
25 Refugees	5 - 7	5 - 7	5 - 7	F and credit	14
26 Fair trade coffee	5 - 7	5 - 7	6 - 7	E onwards	23
27 Population change	5 - 7	5 - 7	5 - 7	E onwards	2
28 Attitudes survey	5 - 7	5 - 7	5 - 7	F and credit	19
29 Development indicators	6 - 7	6 - 7	6 - 7	F onwards	22
30 Global inequality	6 - 7	6 - 7	7	Not part of curriculum but suitable for more able students	2

Contents

Introduction

All the ideas in this book were developed by practising teachers and fully trialled in a range of schools. They provide a series of thought-provoking differentiated activities that enable teachers to incorporate human rights issues into their secondary mathematics classroom. Each activity is accompanied by comprehensive teachers' notes and a resource sheet for photocopying.

It is common to encounter the attitude that there is no connection between human rights and mathematics, which is based on the myth that mathematics is somehow a neutral or value-free subject. However, most current mathematical research (coding theory, for example) is sponsored by the world of e-commerce or military technology. New mathematical developments would appear to be determined by the need to service these industries.

The Eurocentric nature of mathematics generally taught in schools, which tends to ignore contributions made to the subject by other cultures, has been well-documented by several authors. Most people, for example, are not aware that Pascal's Triangle was originally from China or that Pythagoras' Theorem first appeared in the ancient Indian text 'Salbasutras' around 600-800 BC.

Another form of bias in school mathematics is based on gender, with girls continuing to perceive the subject as masculine. This explains why girls perform at a comparable level to boys in mathematics despite outperforming them in almost every other subject at GCSE. There is evidence that girls are more likely to achieve highly in mathematics because they appreciate how important the subject is, whereas boys are more likely to achieve highly because they enjoy the subject. Girls continue to opt for 'A' level and degree level mathematics in fewer numbers than boys.

This book will help to counter-balance the biased nature of mathematics currently taught in schools. Activities with a multicultural focus highlight some of the many contributions made to the subject by people from other parts of the world. Several activities explore gender inequalities in different contexts. Other activities focus on statistics, a branch of mathematics frequently abused by those wishing to promote particular interests or points of view. Care has been taken to avoid tokenistic approaches by concentrating on examples where human rights are inseparable from the mathematical concepts rather than merely used as an 'add-on'.

The preamble to the Universal Declaration of Human Rights calls upon member countries of the United Nations to publicise the text of the declaration and to 'cause it to be disseminated, displayed, read and expounded principally in schools and other institutions'. It is hoped that this book will contribute towards making this goal a reality.

Peter Wright
April 2004

Useful materials

Below is a list of general materials that will be helpful in carrying out the activities in this book. It is advisable to source them before introducing the activities to students.

- Acetate (squared and plain)
- Paper (squared, graph, plain, card)
- 1-100 number grid
- Digit cards
- Calculators
- Atlases
- Access to spreadsheets or graphic calculators or a suitable graphing package
- Rulers, protractors, compasses
- A stock of old newspapers, magazines, books for projects
- Counters
- Cardboard sheets for the board games
- Dice

Foreword

These days Citizenship is popping its head up all across the secondary school curriculum. Teachers will not be at all surprised to find human rights issues being raised in the context of lessons on History, Geography, Religious Education, English or Modern Foreign Languages.*

But human rights and maths – now that's something quite astonishing! Indeed those who look on Mathematics itself as a form of torture (and there are, sadly, quite a few of us about) might find the association of maths with human rights something of an oxymoron.

However this brand new edition of *Human Rights in the Curriculum: Mathematics* brings human rights slap bang into the maths class in a way that is both challenging and exciting. The book has been compiled and trialled by maths teacher and human rights campaigner Peter Wright with a group of fellow maths teacher members of Amnesty International. The first, much praised, edition of this book was published in 1998 (under the title *The Maths and Human Rights Resource Book*) to mark the 50th anniversary of the Universal Declaration of Human Rights (UDHR). The classroom activities in this new edition refer to over half of the 30 Articles of the UDHR, covering civil, political, economic, social and cultural rights.

People queueing to vote in the first democratic non-racial election in South Africa, 1994. This photo can be used to complement Activity 3 on Elections, illustrating how important is the right to vote to those previously denied it.

The UDHR and maths

The UDHR proclaims the universality of human rights, the equal importance of all rights and their interdependence. It extends from the struggle to eliminate torture and discrimination to the fight against poverty, illiteracy and disease and the needs of all people for safety, freedom and dignity. It is hugely relevant in the UK today, for actions that take place thousands of miles away affect our lives as do those that happen here at home. Issues of employment, trade, the environment and justice have global dimensions. The universality of human rights provides a clear set of standards that can be used to discuss the global dimensions of every day life in the UK. Being aware of our rights and responsibilities and those of others is crucial to the development of the knowledge, values and skills of citizenship for life in that wider world.

Some of the world's most celebrated mathematicians have themselves been victims of human rights abuse, prisoners of conscience, torture survivors and victims of unfair trial and execution. Aristotle was sent into exile in 323 BC; Archimedes was slain in Syracuse in 212 BC by a looting Roman soldier while making geometric calculations – although he begged the soldier to wait until he had solved the problem. The German astronomer Johannes Kepler, who wrote on planetary motion, was excommunicated. Galileo Galilei's demonstration of how the earth goes round the sun led to his trial and lengthy imprisonment. Astronomer Giordano Bruno was burned at the stake by the Spanish Inquisition in 1600. Juliusz Schauder disappeared in 1943, probably shot by the Gestapo.

Maths is often required for the determination of human rights. Mathematical processes enable us to understand our world and to see what is happening in it. Without maths we could not analyse patterns and trends. Nor could we work out systems that are impartial, accurate and just – and there are (or should be) a myriad of these: from the calculation of fair wages to the development of fair trade and equal access to resources; from the measurement of illiteracy, poverty, morbidity and mortality in the world to the determination of gender bias, equality and diversity; from the reduction of waste and the organisation of democratic elections, to the analysis of world population growth.

Citizenship and this book

Citizenship education should involve:
• understanding democracy, diversity, fairness, justice, the rule of law and human rights
• the acquisition of values like human dignity, just action, a commitment to equality and concern for human rights
• developing skills, including how to recognise bias and manipulation, the appreciation of the experience and perspective of others, and the ability to identify and influence social, moral and political challenges
• knowledge of human rights documents and issues, the rights and responsibilities of citizens as consumers, employers and as members of families and communities.

Human Rights in the Curriculum: Mathematics examines these human rights challenges and constitutes a valuable contribution to citizenship education. In addition, it is truly multicultural, featuring the ideas and the contributions of mathematical thinkers from many different backgrounds, countries and traditions. The 30 human rights activities that have been selected for this book involve many different mathematical processes and skills, but teachers should note that they do not make up a complete programme of study. Rather they have been designed either to complement existing work or as 'stand alone' activities. Each exercise encourages the students to take an investigative and problem solving approach towards a mathematical topic. They are differentiated and cross-referenced to relevant levels, attainment targets and programmes of study in the Mathematics curricula of England, Scotland, Wales and Northern Ireland.

Dan Jones
Education Adviser, Amnesty International UK
April 2004

---

* See Amnesty International UK's series of teachers' handbooks *Human Rights in the Curriculum* on French, Spanish, History, RE and Geography, published in collaboration with the Education In Human Rights Network.

ACTIVITY 1 Yoruba numbers

Attainment target and levels

England	Number and Calculation	3 - 5
Northern Ireland	Number	3 - 5
Scotland	Number, Money and Measurement	D - F
Wales	Number and Algebra	3 - 5

UDHR Article 27: Everyone has the right freely to participate in the cultural life of the community, to enjoy the arts and to share in scientific advancement and its benefits.
Universal Declaration of Human Rights 1948

Learning objectives
• Calculating using multiples and a combination of addition, subtraction and multiplication.
• Exploring different number systems used by different cultures.
• Target age range: 11-13 years.

Resources
• One copy of the Yoruba numbers activity (page 11) for each student or group of students.
• Calculators may be useful for weaker students.

Description of activity
Students practise using the Yoruba number system based on 20 (vigesimal), which is still in use today. Cowrie shells were the traditional units of currency in West Africa. Because of their advanced trade and commerce developed over 1,000 years ago, the Yoruba needed to count large numbers of cowries. They did this by sorting the cowries into 4 groups of 5 (ie groups of 20).

Students should be familiar with multiples and should revise multiples of 10 prior to trying this exercise. Mental strategies of factors and counting on/back can be introduced here.

They also need to revise 'order of operation', and it is important to clarify with them that the order in which they do things matters.
Example: 2 x 20 – 5 = 35 not 30

Students need to convince themselves that they can find all the Yoruba numbers from 1 to 200 without necessarily writing them all down. They could do this by writing down 20 consecutive Yoruba numbers (eg from 81 to 100) and explaining how to find other Yoruba numbers from

these. Alternatively, they could work in groups, each group finding a different set of 20 consecutive Yoruba numbers. The class could then pool results.

To enrich this exercise, give groups of students a selection of numbers. They could compete in teams to convert them into Yoruba numbers

Solutions
• The Yoruba numbers between 81 and 100 are:

81 = 4 x 20 + 1	91 = 5 x 20 – 10 + 1
82 = 4 x 20 + 2	92 = 5 x 20 – 10 + 2
83 = 4 x 20 + 3	93 = 5 x 20 – 10 + 3
84 = 4 x 20 + 4	94 = 5 x 20 – 10 + 4
85 = 5 x 20 – 10 – 5	95 = 5 x 20 – 5
86 = 5 x 20 – 10 – 4	96 = 5 x 20 – 4
87 = 5 x 20 – 10 – 3	97 = 5 x 20 – 3
88 = 5 x 20 – 10 – 2	98 = 5 x 20 – 2
89 = 5 x 20 – 10 – 1	99 = 5 x 20 – 1
90 = 5 x 20 – 10	100 = 5 x 20

• Yoruba numbers greater than 200 are more difficult to find because there is no Yoruba name for 11. Hence you cannot write 11 x 20. Introduce partitioning as a possible solution. Thus 11 x 20 = (10 + 1) x 20 = 200 + 20 = 220.

Variations
You could compare Yoruba numbers to Mayan numbers (which were also based on 20) or Roman numerals (which also used subtraction).

Ask students to research further into Yoruba numbers. Two useful books are *Africa Counts: Number and pattern in African culture*, Claudia Zaslavsky (Lawrence Hill & Co, 1999) and *Yoruba Numerals*, Robert Armstrong (OUP, 1962).

ACTIVITY 1 Yoruba numbers

The Yoruba people live in parts of Nigeria, Togo and Benin in West Africa. Cowrie shells were the traditional units of currency (ie money) in West Africa. The Yoruba counting system is based on 20 and the Yoruba name for 20 is 'ojun'.

The Yoruba have names for each number from 1 to 10. Numbers greater than 10 are written using multiples of 20.

To write a Yoruba number greater than 10:
• Start with a multiple of 20.
• Either add on 1, 2, 3 or 4,
or subtract 1, 2, 3, 4 or 5.
• You may have to subtract 10 first.
Eg to write 13
• Start with 20
• Subtract 10. So 20 – 10 = 10
• Add 3. 10 + 3 = 13
Thus (1 x 20) – 10 + 3 = 13

Here are some examples of Yoruba numbers:
35 = 2 x 20 – 5
64 = 3 x 20 + 4
73 = 4 x 20 – 10 + 3
109 = 6 x 20 – 10 – 1
140 = 7 x 20
158 = 8 x 20 – 2

• Can you find all Yoruba numbers up to 200?
• Yoruba numbers above 200 are more difficult to find. Can you think of a reason why?

© World Awareness Children's Museum

Rosaline Isikhunnele, age 16: Yoruba Dancers. (Methodist Girls' High School, Lagos, Nigeria 1991)

ACTIVITY 2 Russian multiplication

Attainment target and levels

England	Number and Calculation	4 - 5
Northern Ireland	Number	3 - 5
Scotland	Number, Money and Measurement	E - F
Wales	Number and Algebra	4 - 5

UDHR Article 27: Everyone has the right freely to participate in the cultural life of the community, to enjoy the arts and to share in scientific advancement and its benefits.

Universal Declaration of Human Rights 1948

Learning objectives
• Exploring alternative methods for multiplying together two 2-digit numbers.
• Exploring different approaches to multiplication used in different cultures.
• Target age range: 11-13 years.

Resources
• One copy of the Russian multiplication activity (page 13) and a calculator for each student or group of students.

Description of activity
Note that students need to be familiar with doubling, halving and odd and even numbers.

Students use Russian multiplication as a means of calculation. You may wish to go through another example of Russian multiplication with the whole class to make sure that they understand the method. The exercise should begin with the teacher asking the class to set him/her a problem involving multiplying two two-digit numbers together. The teacher should solve the problem on the board using the method of Russian multiplication and see if the class can guess what is happening prior to explanation.

Then encourage students to set their own Russian multiplication problems (at an appropriate level of difficulty). This exercise is useful for strengthening mental approaches to calculation, so students should only use a calculator to check their answers. Students should be encouraged to work as a team (or in smaller teams) to solve the questions.

A valuable group or class discussion could focus on why this method of multiplication works.

Solutions
The Russian multiplication method will work for any two numbers. The following illustrates why the method works for the example given on the resource sheet:

$$
\begin{aligned}
73 \times 91 &= 72 \times 91 + 91 \\
&= 36 \times 182 + 91 \\
&= 18 \times 364 + 91 \\
&= 9 \times 728 + 91 \\
&= 8 \times 728 + 728 + 91 \\
&= 4 \times 1456 + 728 + 91 \\
&= 2 \times 2912 + 728 + 91 \\
&= 1 \times 5824 + 728 + 91 \\
&= 5824 + 728 + 91 \\
&= 6643
\end{aligned}
$$

Variations
You could use Russian multiplication to multiply together larger numbers: for example, multiply a 2-digit number by a 3-digit number.

You could explore other methods of multiplication used in different cultures, such as the Gelosia (or Chinese) method and the Vedic method (from India). Encourage students to think about which method would be most appropriate for particular multiplication problems.

ACTIVITY 2 Russian multiplication

This method of multiplying two numbers together is traditionally used in Russia. All you need to know is how to double, halve and add!

Here is how to multiply 73 and 91 using Russian multiplication:

Question: 73 x 91

73	91
÷2	x2
36	182
÷2	x2
18	364
÷2	x2
9	728
÷2	x2
4	1456
÷2	x2
2	2912
÷2	x2
1	5824

91 + 728 + 5824 = 6643

Therefore 73 x 91 = 6643

Poster illustrating Russian multiplication

How to do it!

• Halve each number in the left column to get the number below (ignore any half!).
• Double each number in the right column to get the number below.
• Highlight every row where the number in the left column is odd.
• Add the right hand numbers in the highlighted rows only.

Now try some Russian multiplications of your own. You can check your answers with a calculator.

Sofia Kovalevskaya (1850 - 1891)

When Sofia was 11 years old, her bedroom walls were papered with pages of notes on calculus.

However, when she grew up her father would not allow her to leave home to study at a university, and women in Russia could not live apart from their families without the written permission of their father or husband. She was forced to marry so that she could go abroad to enter higher education.

In 1869 Sofia travelled to Heidelberg to study mathematics and the natural sciences, only to discover that women could not matriculate at the university. Eventually she persuaded the university authorities to allow her to attend lectures unofficially, provided that she obtained the permission of each of her lecturers.

She is regarded as one of the world's best mathematicians of her time. She was the first woman member of the Russian Academy of Sciences and the first modern European woman to attain a full professorship.

ACTIVITY 3 Election

Attainment target and levels

England	Number and Calculation	4 - 6
Northern Ireland	Number	4
Scotland	Number, Money and Measurement	E - F
Wales	Number and Algebra	4 - 6

UDHR Article 21: We all have the right to take part in the government of our country. All adults should be allowed to choose the leaders of their country and their representatives.

Universal Declaration of Human Rights 1948

Learning objectives
• Solving problems which involve logic and calculating and ordering with whole numbers.
• Understanding and looking critically at different voting systems.
• Target age range: 12-14 years.

Resources
• One copy of the 'Election' activity (pages 16-17), and information sheet (page 15) and a pair of scissors for each student or group of students.
• Optional: cut out the data from pages 16-17 and photocopy it onto A4 sheets, one per ballot.

Description of activity
Explain the five voting systems described on the information sheet, which are organised into increasing levels of difficulty. You may wish to assign a different voting system to each group of students and ask them to explain their system to the rest of the class.

The calculation should not cause any great difficulty, but you will need to assist pupils in organising the materials before attempting the tasks. The activity becomes more lively if some of the students assume the roles of the candidates.

Students cut out the 11 ballot papers and use them to decide which candidate is elected under each of the voting systems. They need to consider how to arrange the ballot papers in piles and how to tabulate the results of the election.

The results of the election should stimulate discussion around the relative merits of each voting system. Emphasise that the choice of voting system

can influence the outcome of the election (this ballot has been 'rigged' to ensure each candidate is elected under at least one of the systems).

Solutions
• *Relative Majority:* Cortez is elected. Total votes are Ahmed 2, Boateng 3, Cortez 5, Donald 1
• *Absolute Majority:* Boateng is elected. Total votes after 1st round are Ahmed 2, Boateng 3, Cortez 5, Donald 1 (Donald eliminated).
Total votes after 2nd round are Ahmed 3, Boateng 3, Cortez 5 (Ahmed eliminated on 1st round votes).
Total votes after 3rd round are Boateng 6, Cortez 5.
• *Borda Points with Arithmetic Weighting:* Ahmed is elected. Total points are Ahmed 30, Boateng 25, Cortez 26, Donald 29
• *Borda Points with Geometric Weighting:* Cortez is elected. Total points are Ahmed 42, Boateng 38, Cortez 46, Donald 39
• *Condorcet Pair-Wise Counting:* Donald is elected. Eliminate Ahmed and Boateng to give total votes for Cortez 5, Donald 6. Eliminate Ahmed and Cortez to give total votes for Boateng 5, Donald 6. Eliminate Boateng and Cortez to give total votes for Ahmed 5, Donald 6.

Variations
Carry out your own election with students nominating their own candidates (maybe limited to a maximum of five) and designing their own ballot papers. Alternatively, you could vote on 'the best film', 'favourite ice cream', etc. This may also give rise to discussions regarding tactical voting.

You could use other voting systems not included on the information sheet, such as a 'second ballot'.

Useful websites
• Election Reform Society at www.electoral-reform.org.uk
• Inter-Parliamentary Union at www.ipu.org

ACTIVITY 3 Election information sheet

There are many different voting systems. In the UK today we elect MPs through a voting system called Relative Majority or First-Past-the-Post. But different systems were used to elect MPs until 1950. First-Past-the-Post is still not the only available system and it does have some drawbacks. See which system you think is fairest!

Relative Majority

Often called 'First past the post'. Electors have a single vote, shown by an 'X', for one candidate only.
• The candidate with the most votes is elected.
Note: On the resource sheet, assume that the first preference (1) on the ballot papers is the single vote (X).

Absolute Majority (Alternative Vote)

Electors vote for candidates using preferences (the first choice is shown by a '1', the second choice by a '2', and so on).
• The candidate with the fewest first preferences is eliminated.
• Each vote from the eliminated candidate is transferred to the second preference.
• This process is repeated until one candidate has more than half of all votes.
• If two candidates have the same number of votes, then the votes from the previous round(s) are used to work out who is eliminated.

Borda Points with Arithmetic Weighting

Electors vote for candidates using preferences (the first choice is shown by a '1', the second choice by a '2', and so on).
• Points are awarded to candidates, according to the electors' preferences, as shown below.
• If there are four candidates:
4 points are awarded for each first preference
3 points are awarded for each second preference
2 points are awarded for each third preference
1 point is awarded for each fourth preference
• The candidate with the largest points total is elected.
Note: For n candidates, there will be n points for each first preference, n–1 points for each second preference and so on down to 1 point for each nth preference.

Borda Points with Geometric Weighting

Electors vote for candidates using preferences (the first choice is shown by a '1', the second choice by a '2', and so on).
• Points are awarded to candidates, according to the electors' preferences, as shown below.
• If there are four candidates:
8 points are awarded for each first preference
4 points are awarded for each second preference
2 points are awarded for each third preference
1 point is awarded for each fourth preference
• The candidate with the largest points total is elected.
Note: For n candidates, there will be 2^{n-1} points for each first preference, 2^{n-2} points for each second preference and so on down to 1 point (2^0) for each nth preference.

Condorcet Pair-Wise Counting

Electors vote for candidates using preferences (the first choice is shown by a '1', the second choice by a '2', and so on).
• For each pair of candidates, the preferences for those two candidates only are considered.
• If a candidate is preferred to all other candidates, then that candidate is elected.
• If there is no such candidate, then another voting system must be used.
Note: For four candidates, there will be six pairs to consider.

Photocopy original © Amnesty International UK

ACTIVITY 3 Election

Cut out the 11 ballot papers and decide which candidate would be elected under each of these voting systems: Relative Majority; Absolute Majority (Alternative Vote); Borda Points with Arithmetic Weighting; Borda Points with Geometric Weighting; Condorcet Pair-Wise Counting.

Ballot Paper

Place a 1 in the box next to your first preference, a 2 in the box next to your second preference, and so on.

Candidate	
Ahmed (Progressive Party)	3
Boateng (Radical Alliance)	4
Cortez (Independent)	1
Donald (Peoples' Forum)	2

Ballot Paper

Place a 1 in the box next to your first preference, a 2 in the box next to your second preference, and so on.

Candidate	
Ahmed (Progressive Party)	2
Boateng (Radical Alliance)	1
Cortez (Independent)	4
Donald (Peoples' Forum)	3

Ballot Paper

Place a 1 in the box next to your first preference, a 2 in the box next to your second preference, and so on.

Candidate	
Ahmed (Progressive Party)	1
Boateng (Radical Alliance)	3
Cortez (Independent)	4
Donald (Peoples' Forum)	2

Ballot Paper

Place a 1 in the box next to your first preference, a 2 in the box next to your second preference, and so on.

Candidate	
Ahmed (Progressive Party)	3
Boateng (Radical Alliance)	4
Cortez (Independent)	1
Donald (Peoples' Forum)	2

Ballot Paper

Place a 1 in the box next to your first preference, a 2 in the box next to your second preference, and so on.

Candidate	
Ahmed (Progressive Party)	2
Boateng (Radical Alliance)	3
Cortez (Independent)	1
Donald (Peoples' Forum)	4

Ballot Paper

Place a 1 in the box next to your first preference, a 2 in the box next to your second preference, and so on.

Candidate	
Ahmed (Progressive Party)	3
Boateng (Radical Alliance)	1
Cortez (Independent)	4
Donald (Peoples' Forum)	2

ACTIVITY 3 Election (cont)

Ballot Paper

Place a 1 in the box next to your first preference, a 2 in the box next to your second preference, and so on.

Candidate	
Ahmed (Progressive Party)	1
Boateng (Radical Alliance)	2
Cortez (Independent)	4
Donald (Peoples' Forum)	3

Ballot Paper

Place a 1 in the box next to your first preference, a 2 in the box next to your second preference, and so on.

Candidate	
Ahmed (Progressive Party)	3
Boateng (Radical Alliance)	4
Cortez (Independent)	1
Donald (Peoples' Forum)	2

Ballot Paper

Place a 1 in the box next to your first preference, a 2 in the box next to your second preference, and so on.

Candidate	
Ahmed (Progressive Party)	2
Boateng (Radical Alliance)	1
Cortez (Independent)	4
Donald (Peoples' Forum)	3

Ballot Paper

Place a 1 in the box next to your first preference, a 2 in the box next to your second preference, and so on.

Candidate	
Ahmed (Progressive Party)	2
Boateng (Radical Alliance)	3
Cortez (Independent)	4
Donald (Peoples' Forum)	1

Ballot Paper

Place a 1 in the box next to your first preference, a 2 in the box next to your second preference, and so on.

Candidate	
Ahmed (Progressive Party)	3
Boateng (Radical Alliance)	4
Cortez (Independent)	1
Donald (Peoples' Forum)	2

A chance to vote at last: Democracy comes to South Africa in 1994

© Tom Stoddart/Katz

ACTIVITIES

ACTIVITY 4 Egyptian multiplication

Attainment target and levels

England	Number and Calculation	4 - 6
Northern Ireland	Number	5
Scotland	Number, Money and Measurement	E onwards
Wales	Number and Algebra	4 - 6

UDHR Article 27: Everyone has the right freely to participate in the cultural life of the community, to enjoy the arts and to share in scientific advancement and its benefits.

Universal Declaration of Human Rights 1948

Learning objectives

• Exploring an alternative method for multiplying together two 2-digit numbers based on powers of 2.
• Exploring different approaches to multiplication used in different cultures.
• Target age range: 13-15 years.

Resources

• One copy of the Egyptian multiplication activity (page 19) and a calculator for each student or group of students.

Description of activity

Students try out Egyptian multiplication, a method that works for any two numbers. Using this method, any number can be written as the sum of powers of 2 (since every number can be written in binary).

Students need to revise powers before they begin the activity, concentrating on the powers of 2. Encourage them to justify why this method of multiplication works. Show through discussion that the numbers in the left hand column are the powers of 2. This will encourage mental approaches to doubling and addition.

You may wish to go through another example of Egyptian multiplication with the whole class to make sure that they understand the method. Then encourage students to set their own Egyptian multiplication problems (at an appropriate level of difficulty). They should use a calculator only to check their answers.

Solutions

For the example given on the resource sheet:
$53 = 1 + 4 + 16 + 32$ (53 is written as 110101 in binary).
$53 \times 87 = (1 + 4 + 16 + 32) \times 87$

$$= 1 \times 87 + 4 \times 87 + 16 \times 87 + 32 \times 87$$

1	87	+	1	87
2	174			
4	348	+	4	348
8	696			
16	1392	+	16	1392
32	2784	+	32	2784
64	5568		53	4611

Solutions should be fully explained to students using partitioning.

$$53 \times 87 = (1 + 4 + 16 + 32) \times 87$$

By distributive law
$$= 87 \times 1 + 87 \times 4 + 87 \times 16 + 87 \times 32$$
$$= 4611$$

Variations

You could use Egyptian multiplication to multiply together larger numbers, e.g. multiply a 2-digit number by a 3-digit number.

You could explore other methods of multiplication used in different cultures, for example, the Gelosia (or Chinese) method, the Vedic method (from India) and the Russian method (see page 12). Encourage students to think about which method would be most appropriate for particular multiplication problems.

ACTIVITY 4 Egyptian multiplication

This method of multiplying 2 numbers together was used in ancient Egypt. All you need to know is how to double and add!

Here is how to multiply together 53 and 87 using Egyptian multiplication:

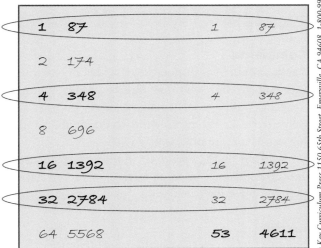

1	87		1	87
2	174			
4	348		4	348
8	696			
16	1392		16	1392
32	2784		32	2784
64	5568		53	4611

• Start with 1 in the left hand column then double each number to get the number below. Continue until the number is greater than 53.
• Double each number in the second column to get the number below.
• Write 53 as the sum of numbers in the left hand column: 53 = 1 + 4 + 16 + 32.
• Highlight every row where the number in the left hand column is included in this sum.
• Add the second column numbers in the highlighted rows only.

87 + 348 + 1392 + 2784 = 4611
Therefore 53 x 87 = 4611

• Try some Egyptian multiplications of your own. Check your answers with a calculator.
• Does the Egyptian method work for all multiplication problems?

This poster depicts an ancient Egyptian pharaoh and queen. The surrounding panels illustrate techniques for counting, working with fractions, solving linear equations, and even computing the area of a circle without using the concept of pi.

Early civilisations

The ancient Egyptians (3rd millenium BC) were able to solve many different kinds of practical mathematical problems, ranging from surveying fields after the annual floods to making the intricate calculations necessary to build the pyramids. Egyptian arithmetic, based on counting in groups of 10, was relatively simple. This base-10 system probably arose for biological reasons, as we have 8 fingers and 2 thumbs. Numbers are sometimes called digits from the Latin word for finger. Unlike our familiar number system, which is both decimal and positional (23 is not the same as 32), the Egyptians' arithmetic was not positional but additive.

Unlike the Egyptians, the Babylonians of ancient Mesopotamia (now Iraq) developed a more sophisticated base-10 arithmetic that was positional, and they kept mathematical records on clay tablets. The most remarkable feature of Babylonian arithmetic was its use of a sexagesimal (base 60) place-valued system in addition to a decimal system. Thus the Babylonians counted in groups of 60 as well as 10. Babylonian mathematics is still used to tell time – an hour consists of 60 minutes, and each minute is divided into 60 seconds – and circles are measured in divisions of 360 degrees.

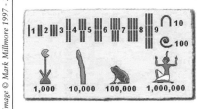

ACTIVITY 5 Kaprekar constant

Attainment target and levels

England	Number and Calculation	4 - 6
Northern Ireland	Number and Algebra	5 - 7
Scotland	Number, Money and Measurement	D onwards
Wales	Number and Algebra	4 - 6

UDHR Article 27: Everyone has the right freely to participate in the cultural life of the community, to enjoy the arts and to share in scientific advancement and its benefits.

Universal Declaration of Human Rights 1948

Learning objectives
• Solving problems involving place value, looking for patterns and using these to generate results.
• Exploring a branch of mathematics developed by a contemporary mathematician from a different culture.
• Target age range: 12-15 years.

Resources
• One copy of the Kaprekar constant activity (page 21) for each student or group of students.
• A spreadsheet (optional).
• Digit cards (optional).

Description of activity
Students conduct a numerical investigation into patterns arising from the difference between the largest and smallest numbers that can be made from any 2, 3, 4 etc digit number.

A useful introductory activity before attempting Kaprekar constant is to explore 2-digit numbers. When you subtract the smallest number from the largest number made from the 2 digits, you will always get a multiple of 9. This is easy to justify algebraically:

$(10a + b) - (10b + a) = 9(a - b)$

Repeating the process will eventually give you 9. (*Trivial exceptions to the above rule are 11, 22, 33, ...*)

Comments
Pupils should be introduced to the idea of creating the largest and smallest number from digits. Teacher could use sets of digit cards to do this, as they are easier for the students to manipulate and make this a more practical activity.

Starting with two-digit numbers, teachers should get pupils to come to the board and help them perform the calculation.

Examples

Number	Largest	Smallest	Difference	
23	32	23	9	
46	64	46	18	
18	81	18	63	
63	63	36	27	
27	72	27	45	
45	54	45	9	Stop

Doing this on the board will encourage the class to see patterns and reinforces what is to be done with three-digit numbers. A spreadsheet solution is good for repeating calculations.

Solutions
• 3-digit numbers always end up as 495.
• 4-digit numbers always end up as 6174 (in no more than 7 steps). 6174 is called the Kaprekar Constant.
• 5-digit numbers end up in a loop.
Trivial exceptions to the above rules are 111, 222, ... , 1111, 2222, ... , 11111, 22222, ...

ACTIVITY 5 Kaprekar constant

D. R. Kaprekar is a modern day Indian mathematician. He discovered the Kaprekar constant in 1949 and Kaprekar numbers in 1980.

Kaprekar constant

• Create a table, with four columns showing Number, Largest, Smallest and Difference.
• Choose any 3-digit number, for example 584, and insert in the column *Number*. Using the 3 digits 5, 8 and 4:
• *Largest* Make the largest number possible (854).
• *Smallest* Make the smallest number possible (458).
• *Difference* Subtract the smallest number from the largest (854 − 458 = 396)
• Now repeat the process, using the number in your *Difference* column (in this case, 396) as your new starting point.
• Keep going … What happens?
• Try starting with other 3-digit numbers.
• What about 4-digit numbers?
• What about 5 digit numbers?

D.R. Kaprekar
Born on January 17, 1905 at a place called Dahanu, near Mumbai, in India. As a child calculations were his hobby. He would spend hours on end trying to solve maths puzzles and problems. As an adult he worked as a mathematician and in 1946 he discovered the 'Kaprekar constant' – the number 6174. He died in 1988.

© *www.liz.richards.btinternet.co.uk/webpage3a.htm*

© Katie Richey/Courtesy of Photoshare, www.photoshare.org

Children attend a government school near Dehradun, Uttaranchal, India. They are told to place their fingers over their mouths when visitors are present so as to keep quiet. 2002

ACTIVITY 6 Kaprekar numbers

Attainment target and levels

England	Number and Calculation	4 - 6
Northern Ireland	Number	6 - 7
Scotland	Number, Money and Measurement	D onwards
Wales	Number and Algebra	4 - 6

UDHR Article 27: Everyone has the right freely to participate in the cultural life of the community, to enjoy the arts and to share in scientific advancement and its benefits.
Universal Declaration of Human Rights 1948

Learning objectives
• Solving problems involving place value and squares, looking for patterns and using these to generate results.
• Exploring a branch of mathematics developed by a contemporary mathematician from a different culture.
• Target age range: 12-15 years.

Resources
• One copy of the Kaprekar numbers activity (page 23) for each student or group of students.
• Spreadsheet (optional).

Description of activity
An investigation into squaring numbers and looking for the relationship between the digits in the square and the original number.

Example

X	X^2	Partitions of X^2
1	1 or 01	$0 + 1 = 1$
(so 1 is a Kaprekar number)		
2	4 or 04	0 + 4 doesn't equal 2
3	9 or 09	0 + 9 doesn't equal 3
4	16	1 + 6 doesn't equal 4
5	25	2 + 5 doesn't equal 5
6	36	3 + 6 doesn't equal 6
7	49	4 + 9 doesn't equal 7
8	64	6 + 4 doesn't equal 8
9	81	$8 + 1 = 9$
(so 9 is a Kaprekar number)		

Do this on the board with the whole class and then divide into groups. Having found the first seven Kaprekar numbers (which are 1, 9, 10, 45, 55, 99, 100), students could return to this work at a later date and search for more numbers. Offer a prize for any student who finds all 20 numbers between 0 and 9999.

Finding Kaprekar numbers can be time-consuming. To avoid students becoming frustrated, you may want to encourage them to share their results or to work in groups. Alternatively, a spreadsheet provides a quick way of comparing each number with its square.

Solutions
The Kaprekar numbers up to 4 figures are: 1, 9, 10, 45, 55, 99, 100, 297, 703, 999, 1000, 2223, 2728, 4879, 4950, 5050, 5292, 7272, 7777, 9999. Some pairs of Kaprekar numbers add up to powers of 10 (eg 1 + 9 = 10, 45 + 55 = 100, 297 + 703 = 1000).

Some Kaprekar numbers are 3 times another Kaprekar number (eg 297 = 3 x 99). These numbers are called Kaprekar triples.

Variations
Try giving students an appropriate selection of Kaprekar numbers and the two rules connecting some Kaprekar numbers described above. Students could then use these rules to generate other Kaprekar numbers.

You could also ask students to write a programme to generate the Kaprekar numbers on a graphic calculator (this challenge is at a significantly higher level than the activity).

ACTIVITY 6 Kaprekar numbers

D. R. Kaprekar is a modern day Indian mathematician. He discovered the Kaprekar constant in 1949 and Kaprekar numbers in 1980.

Kaprekar numbers

To find out if a number is a Kaprekar number, square it, then partition the answer in as many ways as possible, add those parts together and see if the result equals the original number. If it does, then you have found a Kaprekar number!

• 297 is a Kaprekar number because $297^2 =$ 88209 and 88 + 209 = 297.

• Find as many Kaprekar numbers as you can.

• Can you see any connections between different Kaprekar numbers?

D.R. Kaprekar
Born on January 17, 1905 at a place called Dahanu, near Mumbai, in India. As a child calculations were his hobby. He would spend hours on end trying to solve maths puzzles and problems. As an adult he worked as a mathematician and in 1946 he discovered the 'Kaprekar constant' – the number 6174. He died in 1988.

© www.liz.richards.btinternet.co.uk/webpage3a.htm

Example

X	X^2	Partitions of X^2
5	25	2 + 5 doesn't equal 5

(so 5 is not a Kaprekar number)

23	529	52 + 9 doesn't equal 23
		5 + 29 doesn't equal 23

(so 23 is not a Kaprekar number)

87	7569	7 + 569 doesn't equal 87
		75 + 69 doesn't equal 87
		756 + 9 doesn't equal 87

(so 87 is not a Kaprekar number)

297	88209	88 + 209 = 297

(so 297 is a Kaprekar number)

Man standing with a group of children at a village school in Uttar Pradesh, India, 1993

Photocopy original © Amnesty International UK

ACTIVITIES

ACTIVITY 7 Gerrymander

Attainment target and levels

England	Number and Calculation	5 - 7
Northern Ireland	Number and Algebra	7
Scotland	Number, Money and Measurement	F onwards
Wales	Number and Algebra	5 - 7

UDHR Article 21: We all have the right to take part in the government of our country. All adults should be allowed to choose the leaders of their country and their representatives.

Universal Declaration of Human Rights 1948

Learning objectives
• Solving problems involving numbers and logic, looking for patterns and rules.
• Gaining a critical understanding of the relative majority voting system with multiple constituencies.
• Target age range: 13-15 years.

Resources
• One copy of the Gerrymander activity (page 26) and tracing paper for each student or group of students.

Description of activity
Discuss the meaning of the word 'gerrymander'. The dictionary definition is '*To divide the constituencies of a voting area so as to give one party an unfair advantage*'. Ensure that students understand some of the other vocabulary used, such as 'elector', 'constituency'.

You may wish to start by going through a simple example with the whole class. Here is an example you could use: 9 electors vote as follows: A, B, A, B, B, B, A, C, A (arrange randomly). Divide the voters into 3 constituencies so that A is elected.

Encourage students to use tracing paper to solve the problem on the activity sheet. This should give rise to further discussion around the definition of 'gerrymander'. You could ask students to consider which way of drawing the boundaries is the fairest. Draw a comparison between this method of electing representatives and the current election of MPs to the House of Commons.

For solutions see opposite page

ACTIVITY 7 Gerrymander (cont)

Solutions

• See boxes on right. No single party has an overall majority of votes although Party B has more votes than any other party (10 out of 24 or 42%). The third result is particularly unfair as Party A is elected despite having only 6 votes out of 24 (or 25%).

• For 2 parties, the least number of votes needed for a party to be elected is given in the table below.

• For c constituencies and e electors in each constituency, the general rule for the least number of votes needed for a party to be elected is:

$\{Int([c+1]/2) + 1\} \times \{Int([e+1]/2) + 1\}$, where 'Int' is the 'integral part of'. Note: the number of electors = $c \times e$.

Variations

Students could make up similar problems to the initial problem for others to solve.

Investigate for 3 or more parties. For p parties, the general rule for the least number of votes needed for a party to be elected is:

$\{Int([c+1]/p) + 1\} \times \{Int([e+1]/p) + 1\}$, where 'Int' is the 'integral part of'.

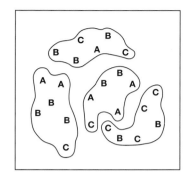

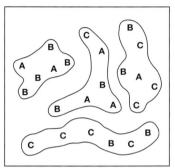

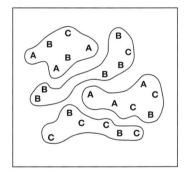

Least number of votes needed to win a two-party election

Number of constituencies	Number of electors in each constituency									
	1	2	3	4	5	6	7	8	9	10
1	1	2	2	3	3	4	4	5	5	6
2	2	4	4	6	6	8	8	10	10	12
3	2	4	4	6	6	8	8	10	10	12
4	3	6	6	9	9	12	12	15	15	18
5	3	6	6	9	9	12	12	15	15	18

ACTIVITY 7 Gerrymander

To *gerrymander* means 'To divide the constituencies of a voting area so as to give one party an unfair advantage'. *(Collins Concise English Dictionary)*

The principle behind gerrymandering is to arrange voting wards in such a way that the 'minority' party has a majority of votes in most of the small wards, while the bulk of the opposition's supporters (the 'majority' party) are corralled in as few large wards as possible. The small wards then elect the same number of representatives to the local government as the larger wards, so that the 'minority' party has control of the corporation or council.

Look at the box below. Twenty-four people wish to elect a party to represent them. Each person can vote for either Party A, Party B or Party C. The boxes represent the votes of the 24 electors. The electors are to be divided into 4 constituencies. Each constituency will have 6 electors. The boundaries of the constituencies must not touch or overlap each other. A party wins a constituency if it has more votes in that constituency than any other party. The party that wins the most constituencies is elected.

• Your job is to draw in the boundaries of the 4 constituencies so that: (1) Party B is elected; (2) Party C is elected; (3) Party A is elected. Now comment on your results.

If there are only 2 parties, Party A and Party B:
• What is the least number of votes that a party could win and still get elected?
• Investigate the least number of votes needed when the number of constituencies and the number of electors are changed.

The term 'gerrymander' derives from an early Republican governor of Massachusetts, Elbridge Gerry. In 1812 the Republican-dominated legislature redrew district lines so that Republicans were more likely to be voted in than Federalists. A Federalist newspaper published the cartoon above showing the strangely-shaped district as a salamander, which the cartoonist dubbed a 'Gerry-mander'. The term stuck.

© AP Louisa Buller, Stringer

In 1998 Dame Shirley Porter was found guilty of trying to rig votes – or gerrymander. Between 1987 and 1989, as Conservative leader of Westminster City Council, she sold council homes at a cheaper price to people who were likely to vote Conservative.

A   C   B
   B   A
A   B   B
   A   B
 B   B
        A
B   B   A   C
   C   A   A
 B   C   C
    C   B   C   B

ACTIVITY 8 Chinese primes

Attainment target and levels

England	Number and Calculation	5 - 7
Northern Ireland	Number and Algebra	6 - 7
Scotland	Number, Money and Measurement	E, F and Credit
Wales	Number and Algebra	5 - 7

UDHR Article 27: Everyone has the right freely to participate in the cultural life of the community, to enjoy the arts and to share in scientific advancement and its benefits.

Universal Declaration of Human Rights 1948

Learning objectives
• Solving problems involving prime numbers and powers of 2.
• Exploring a branch of mathematics developed by a different culture.
• Target age range: 13-15 years.

Resources
For each student or group of students
• One copy of the Chinese Primes activity (page 28).
• Spreadsheet or graphic calculator when investigating Poulet numbers. (NB. A standard calculator with an 8-digit display may only be used to test numbers up to 26.)

Description of activity
Students use the Chinese Hypothesis, developed over 2,000 years ago in China, to test whether or not a number is prime.

Lessons should start with students defining prime numbers. Discuss with them how they might test if a number is prime. Using number grids, students could begin by identifying the primes from 1 to 100 and then testing them using the Chinese hypothesis.

Ensure that students are able to use a spreadsheet or the power feature on their calculator. Start by getting students to generate a list of prime numbers using the Sieve of Eratosthenes or another method.

Solutions
All prime numbers pass the test and therefore satisfy the Chinese Hypothesis. Most non-prime numbers fail the test. However, there are some non-prime numbers that pass the test. These numbers are called Poulet numbers. Examples are 341 (= 11 x 31), 561, 645, 1105, 1387.

Variations
You could tell students that the Chinese Hypothesis is a necessary but not sufficient condition for a number being prime. The activity could then focus on finding the Poulet numbers.

Ask students to write a programme on a graphic calculator for finding prime numbers based on the Chinese Hypothesis.

Photocopy original © Amnesty International UK

Teachers' notes

ACTIVITY 8 Chinese primes

'Chinese mathematics' was defined by the Chinese in ancient times as the 'art of calculation' (*suan chu*). It was seen as both a practical and spiritual art, and covered a wide range of subjects from religion and astronomy to water control and administration.

The following test, sometimes called the Chinese Hypothesis, was invented in China more than 2,000 years ago. The Chinese Hypothesis was designed to test whether or not a number is a prime number.

For any number, n:
- Calculate 2^n (2 raised to the power n).
- Then subtract 2.
- If your answer is divisible by n, then n is a prime number.

Examples
To test if 5 is prime:
$2^5 = 2 \times 2 \times 2 \times 2 \times 2 = 32$
$32 - 2 = 30$
30 is divisible by 5, so 5 is a prime number.

To test if 6 is prime:
$2^6 = 2 \times 2 \times 2 \times 2 \times 2 \times 2 = 64$
$64 - 2 = 62$
62 is not divisible by 6, so 6 is not a prime number.

- Does the test always work?
- Do all prime numbers pass the test?
- Do all non-prime numbers fail the test?

Prime numbers

Many numbers can be made by multiplying smaller numbers together. For example, 3 x 7 = 21

3 and 7 are called factors of 21. But some numbers cannot be made in this way and these are called prime numbers.

A number is called prime if its only factors are one and itself.

The first twelve prime numbers are 2, 3, 5, 7, 11, 13, 17, 19, 23, 29, 31, 37

All prime numbers, apart from 2, are odd numbers.

For a mathematician, the equivalent of breaking the 100 metres world record is to find the highest known prime number. Every year or so, someone discovers a higher one and it gets reported in the newspapers.

In 1989 a team of US computer mathematicians at Amdahl Corporation, California, discovered the (then) highest known prime number (it contains 65,087 digits).

But it has been proved that the number of primes is limitless, so records for the highest known prime can go on being broken forever.

It was back in 230 BC (or thereabouts) that Eratosthenes developed a method for finding all prime numbers!

© Liz Richards

© *www.liz.richards.btinternet.co.uk/uvebpage3a.htm*

Complete turtle Shell

© *www.library.utoronto.caleast/students02/hoi_uan_laifunction.htm*

© *Portland Art Museum, Portland, Oregon. Gift of Mr. Jan Kleijkamp.*

The first true evidence of mathematical activity in China can be found in numeration symbols on tortoise shells and flat cattle bones, commonly called oracle bones, dated from the Shang dynasty (14th century BC). These numerical inscriptions contain both tally and code symbols which are based on a decimal system, and they employed a positional value system. This proves that the Chinese were one of the first civilisations to understand and efficiently use a decimal numeration system.

© *Andrea Fisch/Courtesy of Photoshare, www.photoshare.org*

Adolescent boys working near the Great Wall of China, 1986.

ACTIVITY 9 Amish quilt design

Teachers' notes

Attainment target and levels

England	Shape and Space	3 - 5
Northern Ireland	Shape and Space	4 - 6
Scotland	Shape, Position and Movement	E, F onwards
	(if using rotational symmetry otherwise different mixed levels)	
Wales	Shape, Space and Measures	3 - 5

UDHR Article 18: We all have the right to believe in whatever we wish, to have a faith and to change this if we wish.
Universal Declaration of Human Rights 1948

Learning objectives
• Consolidating understanding of fractions, reflective and rotational symmetry, congruency and similarity.
• Exploring the geometrical properties of a contemporary design from a different culture.
• Target age range: 11-13 years.

Resources
• One copy of the Amish quilt design activity (page 30) for each student or group of students.
• Centimetre squared paper

Description of activity
Before students analyse the quilt design, ensure that they understand the appropriate mathematical vocabulary, such as 'line of symmetry', 'order of rotational symmetry', 'congruent', 'similar'. You could do this by asking the whole class to describe simpler shapes and designs.

Encourage students to use the correct vocabulary when describing the symmetry of the design and when classifying the shapes they can see.

Solutions
• Exactly half of the design is black. Justifying this could promote valuable class discussion during a plenary.
• The design has 4 lines of symmetry and rotational symmetry of order 4.
• There are 8 different sizes of square and 6 different sizes of right-angled isosceles triangles (all similar). There are 10 other sets of similar rectangles with ratios of sides 1:2, 1:3, 1:4, 2:3, 2:5, 2:7, 3:4, 4:5, 4:9, 4:11.

Variations
• How many triangles are there altogether? (There are 72)
• How many squares? (There are 55)
• Explore the mathematical properties of Islamic designs and designs from other cultures.

Photocopy original © Amnesty International UK

ACTIVITY 9 Amish quilt design

The Amish people of North America maintain a simple way of life with few luxuries and strong community links. They use traditional farming and craft methods such as weaving. Amish quilts are an expression of frugality. They have a practical purpose, but the groups of Amish women who make them are also able to socialise and relax. Quilting is a community activity.

Here is a typical design used on an Amish quilt.

Describe the mathematical properties you can see in the Amish quilt design above.
- What fraction of the design is black?
- Does it have reflective symmetry?
- Does it have rotational symmetry?
- How many different shapes can you see?
- Create your own Amish type quilt design.

ACTIVITY 10 Yantras

Attainment target and levels

England	Shape and Space	3 - 5
Northern Ireland	Shape Space and Measure	3 - 5
Scotland	Shape, Position and Movement	D onwards
Wales	Shape, Space and Measures	3 - 5

UDHR Article 18: We all have the right to believe in whatever we wish, to have a faith and to change this if we wish.

Universal Declaration of Human Rights 1948

Learning objectives
• Drawing and describing the symmetry of geometrical designs based on regular polygons inscribed within circles.
• Exploring the geometrical properties of religious symbols and designs.
• Target age range: 11-13 years.

Resources
• One copy of the Yantra activity (page 32), ruler, compasses, angle measurer and coloured pencils for each student or group of students.

Description of activity
A yantra is an image used in meditation, where the symmetrical design encourages peace of mind.

Discuss the symmetry of the first two designs with the whole class. Ensure that students know how to divide the circumference of a circle into equal parts.

The easiest way of doing this is to divide 360 by the number of equal parts and measure this angle at the centre of the circle. This could lead on to a discussion of the internal and external angles of regular polygons. For a hexagon (or equilateral triangle) the following method can also be used. Set the compasses to the radius of the circle. Use the compasses to find successive points on the circumference by drawing an arc centred at each point.

A plenary could focus on how many sets there would be if all students' designs were sorted into sets according to their reflective and rotational symmetry.

Solutions
The first design has rotational symmetry of order 6. It has no reflective symmetry although, before being coloured in, the design had 6 lines of symmetry. The second design has 1 line of symmetry and no rotational symmetry. However, the outer and inner parts of the design taken separately have a lot more symmetry.

Variations
• Explore how the symmetry of the same design may vary depending on how it is coloured in. To do this, it is best to photocopy students' designs before they colour them in.
• Design more complex Yantras by starting with two or more concentric circles.
• Explore the symmetry of symbols and designs from other religions.

Teachers' notes

ACTIVITY 10 Yantras

People have used different forms of meditation for thousands of years. One way of becoming calm is to concentrate your mind on a given object. In Hindu tradition a yantra is used for this purpose. Yantras are based on geometrical patterns constructed within circles.

• Look at the two yantra designs on the right and describe their symmetry.

The illustration below shows you how to create a Yantra type design:

• Draw a circle.

• Divide the circumference of the circle into equal parts (between 3 and 8).

• Join the points to make a regular polygon inscribed within the circle.

• Use the polygon to construct a symmetrical design.

• Colour your design symmetrically.

Create some Yantra type designs of your own. Describe the symmetry of your designs.

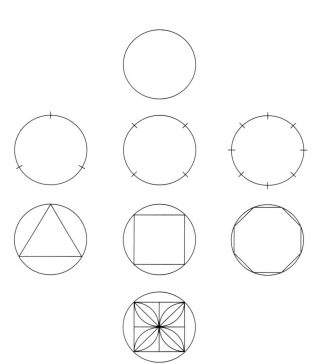

ACTIVITY 11 Bath water

Attainment target and levels

England	Shape and Space	4 - 5
Northern Ireland	Shape, Space and Measure	4 - 6
Scotland	Shape, Position and Movement	D - F
Wales	Shape, Space and Measures	4 - 5

UDHR Article 3: We all have the right to life, and to live in freedom and safety.

Universal Declaration of Human Rights 1948

Learning objectives
• Estimating and approximating using various units of length, volume, distance and time.
• Comparing use of water in the UK with use in countries with more limited access to clean water.
• Target age range: 11-13 years.

Resources
• One copy of the Bath Water activity (page 35) and Bore Hole information sheet (page 41) for each student or group of students.
• Students will need access at home to a bucket and smaller container with a known volume.

Description of activity
Discuss with students how to estimate the volume of water they use for a bath or shower. Then set them the homework task of doing this in reality. Ask them also to check how much water they can carry in their bucket.

Ensure that all students record (or convert) their answers in litres, as this will allow them to compare their results with each other. Check also that they have used an appropriate level of accuracy. You will need to indicate which dimensions should be estimated. Some students may have irregularly shaped baths and it may be difficult for them to estimate. Ask the class to suggest ways to overcome these difficulties. Using an approach similar to the shower would solve this problem. Run taps for one minute and then see how long it would take to run a full bath. It may be useful to give the students a data collection sheet for homework, on which columns can be headed as follows:
• Bath: Length of bath; Width of bath; Height of water in bath; Total volume.

• Shower: Volume in one minute; Number of minutes; Total volume.

Encourage students to compare access to water in the UK with other countries, particularly in the developing world, where access to clean water is more limited. The Bore hole information sheet on page 41 can be used as a prompt for discussion.

It could be useful to carry out the shower calculation in the school using the showers in sports class. This is an excellent opportunity to liaise with the PE department. The students could then calculate how much water the school uses just for showers after sports in a day/week/year etc.

Note: Students should be familiar with the units used in measuring volume and should have carried out some previous work on estimating lengths and calculating volume of 3D objects.

Solutions
1 In the UK, a bath typically uses up to 80 litres of water and a shower up to 35 litres.
2 The students would have to walk 16km (8 trips) to collect enough water for a bath and 8km (4 trips) for a shower. The time would depend upon the speed at which they walked (which would be slower than normal due to the additional weight being carried).

Variations
Students could estimate the amount of water they use altogether in one day. They would need to estimate the volume of water needed for various domestic tasks, such as flushing a toilet (typically 10 litres), washing up (typically 10 litres), washing clothes (a washing machine typically uses 100 litres per cycle). An average person in the UK uses 155 litres of water per day.

Where water is in limited supply, people use it more efficiently. For example, they will often bath using a bucket and ladle or mug. How much water

ACTIVITY 11 Bath water (cont)

would you need to bath in this way?

Ask them to work out how much water is used in washing a car with a hose and how much in watering plants with a watering can, hose or sprinkler.

Research further into the difference in water consumption between the UK and developing countries.

Useful websites

• WaterAid at www.wateraid.org.uk
• Water UK, which represents the UK water industry at www.water.org.uk

ACTIVITY 11 Bath water

Imagine living without access to plenty of clean water – and a separate toilet! But many people around the world have to cope with poverty and disease caused by lack of safe, clean water.

1 Estimate how many litres of water you use when you have a bath or shower.

To estimate the amount of water you use for a bath:

• Estimate the inside length and width of your bath.

• Estimate the height of water you normally have in the bath.

• Calculate an approximate value for the volume of water used (volume = length x width x height).

To estimate the amount of water you use for a shower:

• Use a bucket to collect the water that runs from the shower in one minute.

• Estimate the volume of water in the bucket by using a container whose volume you know, such as a milk carton or water bottle.

• Estimate the number of minutes you normally spend in the shower.

• Calculate an approximate value for the volume of water used (volume = water in bucket x number of minutes).

2 Imagine you are in an area where there is no piped water. Your nearest water supply is one kilometre away. You have to collect all the water you need by carrying it in your bucket, which holds 10 litres. Many people in the world, particularly in developing countries, collect their water in this way.

Try it out for yourself: using a bucket, find out how many litres of water you can comfortably carry without spilling it.

• How many trips would you need to make to the water supply to get enough water for a bath or shower?

• How far would you need to walk and how long would it take you?

© CCP/Courtesy of Photoshare, *www.photoshare.org*

Pakistan: Woman carrying a jar of water on her head passing a cow as it walks into a body of water.

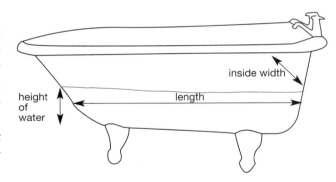

Photocopy original © Amnesty International UK

ACTIVITY 12 How big is the world?

Attainment target and levels

England	Shape and Space	4 - 5
Northern Ireland	Shape, Space and Measure	4 - 6
Scotland	Shape, Position and Movement	E onwards
Wales	Shape, Space and Measures	4 - 5

UDHR Article 2: These rights belong to everybody, whatever our differences.

Universal Declaration of Human Rights 1948

Learning objectives

• Finding approximations for the areas of irregular shapes by counting whole and part squares and calculating using ratio and proportion.
• Comparing a Peters Projection map of the world with more traditional Eurocentric maps.
• Target age range: 12-14 years.

Resources

For each student or group of students:
• One copy of the How Big is the World? activity (page 37)
• Peters Projection map (page 38), enlarged to A3 if desired.
• At least one other map.
• Squared acetate paper and dry wipe pens. (You could use tracing paper instead, but this is time-consuming and might encourage inaccuracy.)

Description of activity

Through mathematical comparisons of different areas and maps, students gain an awareness of land and territory representation and misrepresentation.

At first sight the Peters Projection map may look strange to students. Explain how it is the only map of the world to show the areas of different countries in true proportion. Other maps tend to make Europe and North America look larger than they really are when compared with Africa, South America and South Asia.

Comparing the areas of the irregular shapes is best tackled through class discussion. Ask students to count the whole squares and then count only those part squares where more than half of the square is enclosed within the shape. Alternatively, count all part squares, halve this number and then add the number of whole squares. Using either

method, the first shape has a larger area than the second. Discuss why both methods work and why they are only approximations.

When comparing the areas of the countries, students should work in pairs. One student overlays the acetate over the shapes and maps and also counts the squares. The other records the area. They then change roles. Giving them a data sheet for collection will help them to organise the work.

The data sheet could include colums with these headings: Country; Number of whole squares; Number of part squares; Total area (km^2).

Some students may calculate the areas of each country directly using ratios. Others can use the area of Mexico first to calculate the area that each square represents. You might wish to discuss appropriate degrees of accuracy for the areas, bearing in mind that students are using an approximate method.

Solutions

The countries are listed below in size order of area, with the largest first. The number in brackets shows approximately how many times bigger the country is than the UK: India (13 times bigger); Argentina (11); Sudan (10); Mexico (8), Angola (5); Spain (2). These results will not be true for other maps of the world, for the reasons given above.

The approximate areas are India 3,290,000 km^2, Argentina 2,770,000 km^2, Sudan 2,510,000 km^2, Angola 1,250,000 km^2, Spain 510,000 km^2, United Kingdom 240,000 km^2. Students' results will depend upon their estimates for the relative areas.

Variations

Explore the areas of other countries and different continents and the extent to which these are misrepresented on various maps. To further investigate misrepresentation try sourcing some different maps produced in other countries. Liaison with the geography and/or language departments may prove helpful.

ACTIVITY 12 How big is the world?

Maps of the world are not as accurate as you might expect, because it is so difficult to show a round world on a flat surface. The Peters Projection map may look strange, but it is the only map that shows the land areas of different countries in true proportion.

• It is possible to compare the area of two irregular shapes by overlaying them with squared acetate paper, counting the squares where more than half of the square is covered by the shape, and recording the total area (the number of squares).

Alternatively you can use tracing paper to trace the shapes and then place the tracing paper on top of squared paper – but beware of inaccuracy!

• Which of the two shapes below has the largest area? Why?

• Using the Peters Projection map of the world, compare the areas of the United Kingdom and the following six countries: Angola, Argentina, India, Mexico, Spain, Sudan.
• List the countries in order of area (largest first).
• Approximately how many times bigger than the UK is each country?
• Do you get the same answers if you use a different type of map of the world?
• The area of Mexico is approximately 1,960,000 km^2. Use this to find the approximate area of each of the other countries.

© Maillard J, 1996

Girl working in the fields in Senegal

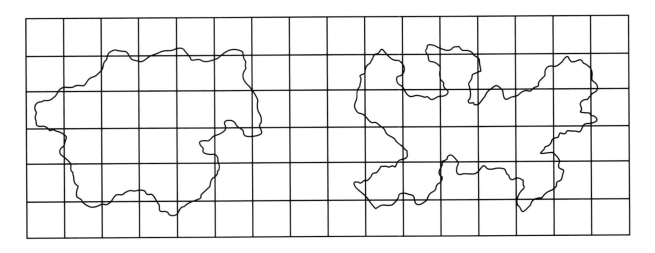

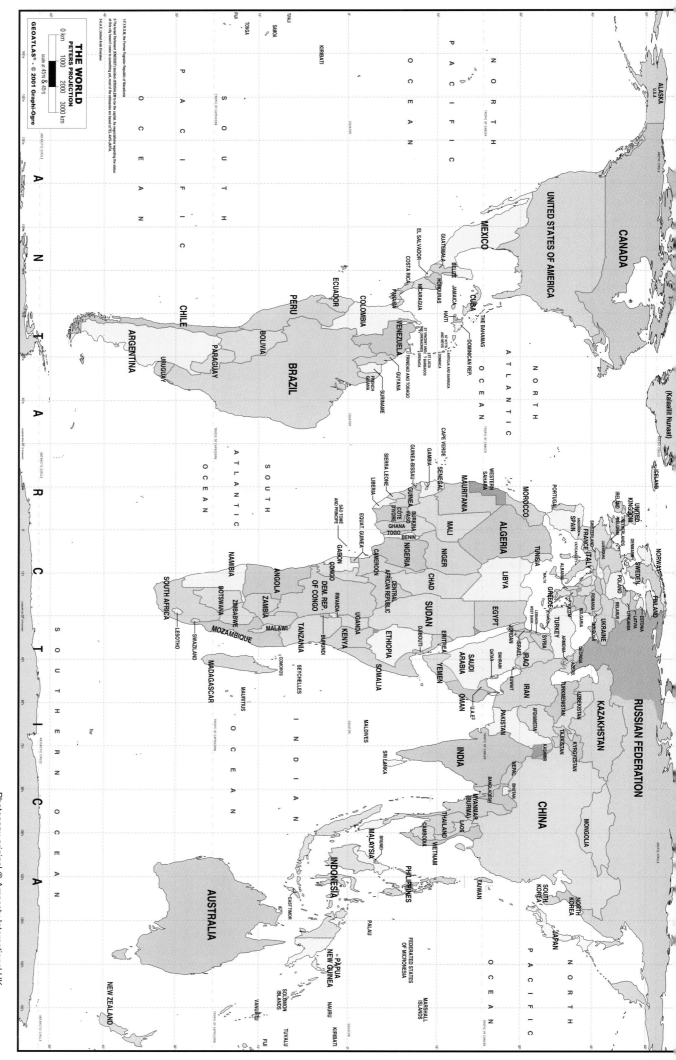

ACTIVITIES

THE WORLD
PETERS PROJECTION

GEOATLAS® - © 2001 Graph-Ogre

Scale at 45°N & 45°S

0 km 1000 2000 3000 km

1-F.Y.R.O.M. the Former Yugoslav Republic of Macedonia.
2-The Israel Parliament (KNESSET) decided JERUSALEM to be the capital. As negotiations regarding the status of this city haven't come to something yet, most of the embassies are based at TEL-AVIV-JAFFA.
3-U.A.E.: United Arab Emirates.

ACTIVITY 13 Bore hole

Attainment target and levels

England	Shape and Space & Handling Data	4 - 6
Northern Ireland	Shape, Space and Measure & Handling Data	5
Scotland	Shape, Position and Movement & Information Handling	E, F and General or Credit
Wales	Shape, Space and Measures & Handling Data	4 - 6

UDHR Article 17: Everyone has the right to own things or share them.

UDHR Article 24: We all have the right to rest from our work, to relax and have holidays.

Universal Declaration of Human Rights 1948

Learning objectives

- Solving problems involving minimising the sum of decimal numbers and looking for a general rule (based on the median).
- Gaining an insight into the limited access to clean water in many developing countries.
- Target age range: 13-15 years.

Resources

- One copy of the Bore hole activity (page 40) and information sheet (page 41) for each student or group of students.
- Spreadsheet (optional).

Description of activity

Through discussion and mathematical problem-solving, students identify the best place for a village of five families to dig a bore hole. They then move on to work on a different set of data.

Before starting this activity, discuss with students the lack of access to clean water in many developing countries, using the information sheet as a prompt. You should then ensure that all students understand the layout of the village and the positions of the houses shown in the diagram.

It may help students to start by drawing a sketch of the village. The calculations are repetitive, so you may wish students to use a spreadsheet to generate their results. It is important that they have a number of examples to work on in order to see a pattern.

Solutions

For a village of five families (as in the illustration), the bore hole should be built 1.9 km from the stream next to the home of Chanda's family (total distance = 0.6 + 0.2 + 0 + 0.3 + 0.5 = 1.6 km). In general, the bore hole should be built next to the home of the middle family (anywhere between the homes of the middle two families if the number of families is even). Therefore the median of the distances the families live from the stream will give a sensible position to build the bore hole.

Variations

Suppose there were three families living at the corners of a piece of land in the shape of a scalene triangle. The instinctive response is to build the bore hole at the 'centre' of the triangle. However, there are several definitions for the 'centre' of a triangle. Which of these should be used? The correct answer is at the 'Steiner Point' (the point where, if lines are drawn to each vertex, the angle between the lines will be 120 degrees). To find the Steiner Point, construct an equilateral triangle on each side of the scalene triangle. Use the new vertex of each equilateral triangle as the centre of an arc passing through the other 2 vertices. These 3 arcs intersect at the Steiner Point.

Other 'centres' to explore are the 'centroid' (where the 3 lines joining each vertex to the mid-point of the opposite side intersect), the point equidistant from the 3 vertices (where the perpendicular bisectors of the 3 sides intersect) and the point equidistant from the 3 sides (where the 3 angle bisectors intersect). They will need to use accurate construction methods and measurement.

Research further into the inequality in access to clean water between the UK and developing countries.

Useful websites

- WaterAid at www.wateraid.org.uk
- Water UK at www.water.org.uk

Photocopy original © Amnesty International UK

ACTIVITY 13 Bore hole

Sinaga is a small village in the West of Kenya. There is no piped water supply so villagers have to carry all the water they need from a stream. Five families in Sinaga have been saving up and they now have enough money between them to build a bore hole. This will save them time and also allow them to pump up clean water which will improve their health.

All five families live along the same straight road which crosses the stream at one end of the village. Anyargo's family live 1.3 km from the stream, Bwogo's family 1.7 km, Chanda's family 1.9 km, Dunga's family 2.2 km and Enok's family 2.4km from the stream. They agree that the bore hole should be built beside the road.

• Where should they build the bore hole so that the total distance the five families must walk to the bore hole is as small as possible?

• Try changing the distance of each family from the stream. Where should the bore hole be built now?

• What if there were 3 families, 4 families, 6 families, etc?

© www.luko2004.org.uk/ pages/pictures2.htm, 2004

Pumping water from the local bore hole in Lukotaime, a small village in Uganda.

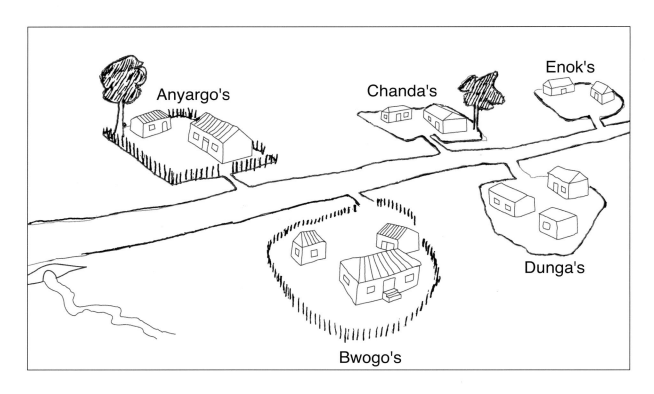

ACTIVITY 13 Bore hole information sheet

Water supply

In 1994, only 46 per cent of people in Africa had access to safe drinking water. This is also a serious problem in parts of Asia and South America. The burden of collecting water falls mainly on women and children. In Kenya, 95 per cent of the water for the home is collected by women, who spend as much as five hours each day collecting water, often walking several kilometres to find it. One way of providing clean water is to build a bore hole. This involves digging a shaft down to the water table which allows clean water to be pumped up from deep underground.

Water and human rights

Access to clean water and sanitation is today considered as a basic necessity. We each need three litres of water a day just to survive. For drinking, preparing food, bathing and personal hygiene, a minimum of 50 litres a day is needed. Poor people have less access to public water supplies and are often forced to buy from private vendors. They may end up paying more for their water than those with a piped supply. The burden of debt carried by some poor countries makes it difficult for their governments to allocate the resources needed to improve supplies.

Water and health

The lack of a clean water supply is the cause of 250 million cases of disease worldwide each year, which lead to more than five million deaths. Diseases such as cholera, typhoid, dysentery and diarrhoea could be virtually eliminated by providing access to clean drinking water and adequate sanitation. Water collected from streams, for example, is often contaminated because the same stream may be used by people for washing and bathing and by animals for drinking.

Water and the environment

Water supplies in many parts of the world are becoming scarcer. This may be due to population growth, as well as deforestation, pollution, dams and irrigation. Water supplies to industry and agriculture are often given a higher priority than supplies to households. It is now increasingly important not just to improve supplies, but to be more efficient and reduce the amount of water we use.

Water and development

Governments need to subsidise supplies to ensure that everyone, including poor people, has access to clean water and sanitation. Local communities, including both women and men, must be involved in planning development projects and finding solutions. Education can play a crucial role in helping communities take the necessary steps to improve their water supply and ensure it is used efficiently.

Slamet Rahardjo/Courtesy of Photoshare, www.photoshare.org

Stills from the *Equatorial Trilogy*, a set of three videos filmed in Indonesia. Both photos are on this page are from *Anak Hilang* ('Lost Child'), a story of the people who live in a slum neighbourhood built above a filthy estuary in Jakarta. 1992.

ACTIVITY 14 Magic dominoes

Attainment target and levels

England	Using and Applying Mathematics	3 - 5
Northern Ireland	Processes in Mathematics	3 - 5
Scotland	Problem-solving	C onwards
Wales	Using and Applying Mathematics	3 - 5

UDHR Article 27: Everyone has the right freely to participate in the cultural life of the community, to enjoy the arts and to share in scientific advancement and its benefits.

Universal Declaration of Human Rights 1948

Learning objectives

• Solving problems involving the properties of magic squares.
• Exploring a branch of mathematics developed by a different culture.
• Target age range: 11-13 years.

Resources

• One copy of the Magic dominoes activity (page 43) for each student or group of students.
• Either a standard 6-dot set of dominoes or get the students to cut out the domino pieces from the activity sheet.

Description of activity

Ask your students to solve two problems from China. First, they must arrange six dominoes to make a 3 by 3 magic square (where each row, column and diagonal adds up to 9). Then ask them to arrange 8 dominoes to make a 4 by 4 magic square (where each row, column and diagonal adds up to 19).

You may wish students to compare their solutions. This may lead to valuable discussion on congruency (ie one solution may be a reflection or a rotation of another).

Solutions

One possible solution to each of the two problems is shown here:

1

2	5	2
3	3	3
4	1	4

2

6	4	6	3
3	5	5	6
4	5	4	6
6	5	4	4

Variations

Use a standard 6-dot set of dominoes to make some more magic squares. It is possible to use all 28 dominoes to make a 7 by 7 magic square.

You could use a spreadsheet to allow students to try out different combinations, showing the totals for rows, columns and diagonals in appropriate cells.

Teachers' notes

ACTIVITY 14 Magic dominoes

Chinese mathematicians have studied both dominoes and magic squares for many centuries. The two puzzles below involve using dominoes to make magic squares.

Magic squares

A magic square is a square array of numbers arranged in such a way that the sum of each row, each column and both diagonals is constant. They are called magic squares because there are so many relationships between the sums of the numbers filling the squares.

Magic squares are very old. The first known magic square was discovered in China on a scroll by the river Loh, now known as the Yellow River. It was called Loh-Shu. The invention of the scroll was attributed to Fuh-Hi, the mythical founder of the Chinese civilisation, who lived 2858-2738 BC. All the odd numbers, the yang symbols, represented heaven. All the even numbers, the yin symbols, represented earth.

Dominoes

The game of dominoes originated in China in ancient times and came to Europe only in the middle of the 18th century. The first European pieces had ivory faces with ebony backings. It is thought that they got their name because of their resemblance to the hooded cloak called a domino.

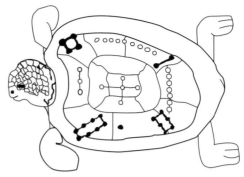

© *The Math Forum, Drexel University/ Linda Braatz-Brown*

The oldest known magic square, called Lo-Shu, appeared on the back of a divine turtle in the river Loh over 4,000 years ago

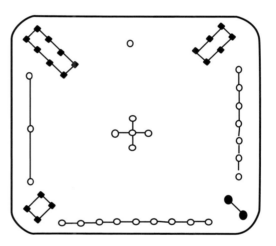

An example of a magic square

© *danil 1999-2003 www.magic-squares.de/general/squares/squares.html*

1 Arrange these 6 dominoes to make a 3 by 3 magic square. Each row, column and diagonal must add up to 9. You will need to place all the blanks together in one column, which is not counted as part of the magic square.

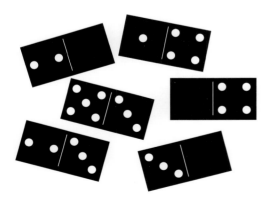

2 Arrange these 8 dominoes to make a 4 by 4 magic square. Each row, column and diagonal must add up to 19.

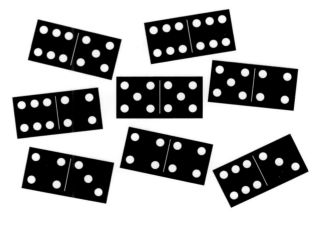

Teachers' notes

ACTIVITY 15 Ayo

Attainment target and levels

England	Using and Applying Mathematics	4 - 5
Northern Ireland	Processes in Mathematics	4 - 5
Scotland	Problem-solving	E onwards
Wales	Using and Applying Mathematics	4 - 5

UDHR Article 27: Everyone has the right freely to participate in the cultural life of the community, to enjoy the arts and to share in scientific advancement and its benefits.
Universal Declaration of Human Rights 1948

Learning objectives
• Playing a game based upon counting and looking for winning strategies.
• Exploring a mathematical game originating from a different culture.
• Target age range: 12-14 years.

Resources
• One copy of the Ayo activity (page 45) and 48 counters for each pair or group of students.
• Egg cartons (optional).

Description of activity
The traditional Nigerian game of Ayo encourages students to work in teams and enjoy themselves while discussing and developing mathematical strategies.

First organise students into pairs or small groups. Playing in teams of two or more, rather than as individuals, will help to stimulate discussion of strategies. Egg cartons and counters could be used to model the board and pebbles. Alternatively students could draw 12 large circles on paper to represent the board.

Ensure that students understand the rules before they start playing. You could use an overhead projector and a transparency with a representation of the board and counters to explain the rules. If there are differing interpretations of the rules, encourage students to agree amongst themselves how to resolve them. A plenary discussion could focus on possible winning strategies.

Solutions
None required.

Variations
Students could play similar games such as Oware (from Ghana) and Mbao (from Kenya). They will first need to carry out research in order to find the rules.

Students may wish to invent their own games by agreeing a different set of rules.

ACTIVITY 15 Ayo

Ayo is a traditional game for two from Nigeria. Similar games can be found in many parts of Africa and Asia, although the names and rules may vary. Ayo is played on a wooden board with 12 holes carved out, using pebbles or dried beans.

The rules of Ayo

• Start with 4 pebbles in each hole on the board.
• The aim is to collect as many pebbles as possible.
• Players take it in turns to have a go.
• On your go, pick up all the pebbles from any hole on your side of the board. Place one pebble in each adjacent hole, counting in a clockwise direction.
• If you place the last pebble in a hole on your opponent's side of the board, which already contains 1 or more pebbles, then you collect all the pebbles from that hole.
• If you have placed a pebble in any other hole on your opponent's side of the board, which already contained 1 or more pebbles, then you also collect all the pebbles from that hole.
• You must not leave your opponent without any pebbles on their side of the board unless there is no other option.
• If it is not possible to move any of the pebbles on your side of the board into your opponent's side, then you collect all the pebbles on your side.
• The winner is the player who has collected the most pebbles at the end of the game.

Clay sculpture from Nigeria, possibly the Benin culture, because of the shape of the game board.

Ayo board and pebbles

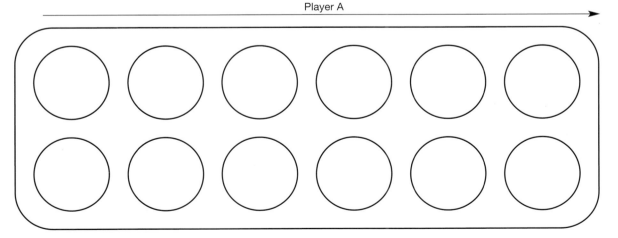

Player A

Player B

ACTIVITY 16 Brahmagupta's problem

Attainment target and levels

England	Number and Calculation	4 - 5
Northern Ireland	Number and Algebra	6 - 7
Scotland	Problem-solving	E onwards (General if formula not used)
Wales	Number and Algebra	4 - 5

UDHR Article 27: Everyone has the right freely to participate in the cultural life of the community, to enjoy the arts and to share in scientific advancement and its benefits.

Universal Declaration of Human Rights 1948

Learning objectives

• Solving problems involving fractions and the lowest common multiple.

• Exploring problems written by a mathematician from a different culture.

• Target age range: 13-15 years.

Resources

• One copy of Brahmagupta's problem activity (page 47) for each student or group of students.

Description of activity

This is an entertaining problem-solving activity based on a formula devised 1,400 years ago by the Indian mathematician Brahmagupta. Once students have solved it, encourage them to justify their answer algebraically.

Encourage the students to try different approaches, such as trial and error, algebra and lowest common multiple. Have in hand a stock of several similar problems to allow the class to practise before asking them to make up their own problems.

Students should be confident in calculating with fractions and solving simple algebraic equations of the following type:

Example 1: Brahma gave out all the apples in a bag. He gave $\frac{1}{2}$ to Rupa, $\frac{1}{4}$ to Bashir, $\frac{1}{5}$ to Gita and kept 20 for himself. How many apples were there in the bag to start with? Answer = 400.

Example 2: Brahma gave out all the apples in a bag. He gave $\frac{1}{5}$ to Rupa, $\frac{1}{3}$ to Bashir, $\frac{1}{6}$ to Gita and kept 162 for himself. How many apples were there in the bag to start with? Answer = 540

Solutions

There are several ways of solving Brahmagupta's problem, but most use the fact that the lowest common multiple of 3, 4 and 5 is 60. One possible method is shown below:

Suppose that the number of apples in the bag is N.

Then the number of apples that Brahma gave away is:

$\frac{1}{3}N + \frac{1}{4}N + \frac{1}{5}N = \frac{20}{60}N + \frac{15}{60}N + \frac{12}{60}N = \frac{47}{60}N$

The number of apples left in the bag is:

$N - \frac{47}{60}N = \frac{13}{60}N$

Brahma kept 13 apples for himself, therefore

$\frac{13}{60}N = 13$ and hence N = 60.

Variations

Students could think up their own, similar problems. They could solve these and then justify their solutions to the whole class.

ACTIVITY 16 Brahmagupta's problem

Brahmagupta was born in 598 AD in northwest India. He became a very important mathematician and astronomer, whose work is still used today. The problem on this page is based on one that he devised 1,400 years ago. See if you can solve it!

- Brahma gave out all the apples in a bag.
- He gave one third to Rupa.
- He gave one quarter to Bashir.
- He gave one fifth to Gita.
- He kept 13 for himself.

- How many apples were there in the bag to start with?

Women carrying sticks, India

Our present number system traces back to India in the 3th century BC and this poster emphasises the important contributions made by Indian culture to astronomy, geometry, and the theory of numbers.

The famous 14th century stone chariot at Hampi, Karnataka, India

ACTIVITY 17 Totolospi

Attainment target and levels

England	Using and Applying Mathematics	5 - 7
Northern Ireland	Processes in Mathematics	5 - 7
Scotland	Problem-solving	F and Credit
Wales	Using and Applying Mathematics	5 - 7

UDHR Article 27: Everyone has the right freely to participate in the cultural life of the community, to enjoy the arts and to share in scientific advancement and its benefits.

Universal Declaration of Human Rights 1948

Learning objectives
• Playing and analysing a game based upon probability.
• Exploring a mathematical game originating from a different culture.
• Target age range: 13-15 years.

Resources
• One copy of the Totolospi activity (page 49), counters and three wooden dowels for each pair or group of students. (You could substitute drawing pins for the dowels – see Variations.)

Description of activity
Organise students into pairs or small groups to play Totolospi using the illustration on the resource sheet. Ensure that students understand the rules and allow them to play the game until they can begin to predict different outcomes.

Then encourage students to analyse the probabilities involved in the game. Ask them to find the experimental probability of a single dowel landing flat side face up by carrying out an appropriate number of trials. They could then use this to calculate the probability of all three dowels landing flat/round side facing up. A plenary discussion could focus on how many moves you would expect to make before completing the game.

Solutions
Suppose the probability of a single dowel landing flat side up is p. Then the probability of all three dowels landing flat side up is p^3 and the probability of all three dowels landing round side up is $(1 - p)^3$.

Variations
You could substitute the three dowels with three similar objects that have two outcomes with unequal probabilities, such as three drawing pins or three bottle tops.

Students could invent their own rules for the game, bearing in mind what they have learnt about the probabilities involved. They may wish to vary the number of counters, the number of dowels, the number of spaces moved for different outcomes, or the design of the board.

ACTIVITY 17 Totolospi

Totolospi is a traditional game for two to four players invented by the Hopi people (native Americans). It is played on a board similar to that shown, using counters and three wooden dowels (with a semi-circular cross-section).

The rules of Totolospi:
• Each player starts by placing their counter on one of the black circles.
• The aim is to reach the black circle on the opposite side of the board.

• Players take it in turns to have a go.
• When it is your go, you throw the 3 dowels.
• If all 3 dowels land with the flat sides facing up, then you move your counter one space.
• If all 3 dowels land with the round sides facing up, then you move your counter two spaces.
• For any other combination you do not move at all.
• The winner is the first player to move their counter to the black circle on the opposite side of the board.

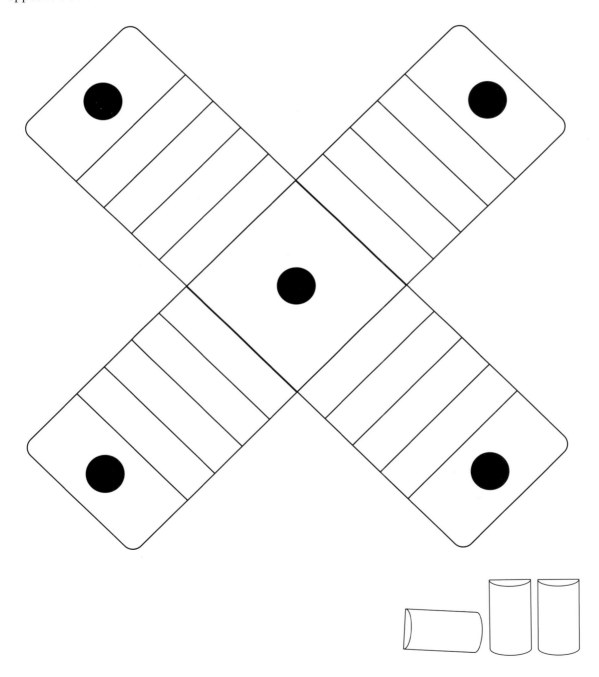

ACTIVITY 18 Life expectancy

Attainment target and levels

England	Handling Data	3 - 5
Northern Ireland	Handling Data	4 - 5
Scotland	Information Handling	C onwards
Wales	Handling Data	3 - 5

UDHR Article 25: We all have the right to enjoy a good life. Mothers, children, the elderly, the unemployed and the disabled have the right to be cared for.

UDHR Article 3: We all have the right to life, and to live in freedom and safety.

Universal Declaration of Human Rights 1948

Learning objectives
• Collecting data from a secondary source, drawing and interpreting a bar chart.
• Comparing life expectancies in various countries in different parts of the world.
• Target age range: 11-13 years.

Resources
• One copy of the Life expectancy activity (page 51) and a spreadsheet or graph paper for each student or group of students.
• Copies of world development statistics (see Appendix 1, page 77) or access to data from an alternative source, such as the Internet.

Description of activity
Students use bar charts to interpret and compare life expectancies in different countries. It is important that students are familiar with bar charts.

You may wish to discuss the initial question on the activity sheet with the whole class. Appropriate responses might include: 'Japan has the highest life expectancy'; 'Sierra Leone has the lowest life expectancy'; 'The range of the life expectancies is 43 years'.

Ask the students to compare the life expectancies of people living in different countries and continents. Suggest that they choose countries from the 'industrialised' world and the 'developing' world. They can use the Appendix or the Internet to find the life expectancies.

Encourage the students to use a spreadsheet to record their results and to draw their bar charts.

The final question on the resource sheet could provide a focus for a plenary discussion. Possible

factors that might affect life expectancy are: war; natural disasters; nutrition; diseases; healthcare provision; access to safe drinking water; working conditions; housing and social welfare. All of these are directly or indirectly related to poverty.

Solutions
The values used to produce the bar chart on the resource sheet are for 1999: Bangladesh (59 years), Bolivia (62 years), Japan (81 years), Morocco (67 years), Poland (73 years), Sierra Leone (38 years).

Variations
Students could use bar charts to compare a different development indicator for countries of their choice. Indicators with integer values below 100 are easiest to use, for example, literacy rates, primary enrolment ratios and infant mortality rates.

Multiple bar charts can be used to compare factors such as male and female life expectancy or adult literacy.

Students will gain a better understanding of how different life is for people living in different countries if you ask them to use their spreadsheets to perform additional calculations, such as finding:
• Mean life expectancy for Europeans, Asians, Australasians etc
• Range of life expectancies across specific areas (e.g. continents)
• Modal life expectancy

These calculations can be performed on all the development indicators. A useful extension would be to use scatter graphs to compare development indicators, and look for link between e.g. infant mortality and life expectancy.

Useful websites
• United Nations Development Programme at www.undp.org Navigate to the latest Human Development Report, then to Human Development Indicators. (It is useful to make a back-up copy of the relevant web wages.)

ACTIVITY 18 Life expectancy

Life expectancy in a country is the average number of years a newborn child can expect to live, assuming that the living conditions in that country do not change.

The bar chart below shows average life expectancy in six countries from different parts of the world. Look at the chart, then answer the questions on the right.

- What does the bar chart tell you about life expectancy in the six countries?
- Choose some countries from different parts of the world.
- Find the life expectancy in each country.
- Represent this data in a bar chart.
- What does your bar chart show?
- What factors do you think might cause a country to have a high life expectancy or a low life expectancy?

Life expectancies of selected countries

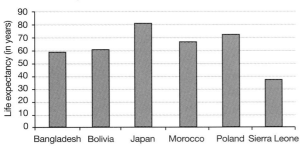

ACTIVITIES

Uganda 1990: Suna holding his baby, both infected with HIV. Video still from *It's Not Easy*, the first HIV/AIDS drama produced in Africa. Suna is a young business executive with several girlfriends, who ignores warnings about AIDS. When his wife and baby become ill, he learns that he has infected them with HIV. He must also face the prejudices of his co-workers while learning to deal with his illness. Suna turns his despair into hope and determination for those around him.

ACTIVITY 19 Fair trade chocolate

Attainment target and levels

England	Handling Data & Number and Calculation	4 - 6
Northern Ireland	Handling Data & Number	5 - 6
Scotland	Information Handling & Number, Money and Measurement	D onwards
Wales	Handling Data & Number and Algebra	4 - 6

UDHR Article 23: Every adult has the right to a job, to a fair wage for their work and to join a trade union and choose what work they do.

Universal Declaration of Human Rights 1948

Learning objectives

• Representing data in a compound bar chart and calculating using percentages.
• Comparing how much of the price you pay goes to the producers for fair trade and other products.
• Target age range: 11-13 years.

Resources

• One copy of the Fair trade chocolate activity (page 53) and information sheet (page 54) for each student or group of students.
• Spreadsheets (optional).
• Chocolate bar wrappers (optional).

Description of activity

Students calculate where their money goes if they buy an ordinary bar of chocolate and if they buy fair trade chocolate. Ensure that students understand how the length of the typical chocolate bar has been divided into the correct proportions (measuring with a ruler may help). Choosing an appropriate length for the chocolate bar, for example 10cm, makes the calculations easier.

You may wish to show students examples of wrappers from fair trade chocolate bars to help them identify them in a shop or supermarket. You could set students the task of finding prices for homework. It may be worth carrying out your own research into prices to act as back-up data.

The activity sheet concentrates on one aspect only of fair trade. Use the information sheet as a focus for a plenary discussion with students in order to gain a fuller understanding of fair trade.

You could address some of the following issues in the plenary discussion. Whilst the company's share in the price of a fair trade chocolate bar is much less than for a typical chocolate bar, the shop or supermarket's share is much higher (because fair trade products are sold in much lower quantities to what is seen as a niche market and the prices are increased accordingly) and the other ingredients and costs are much higher (because processing and transportation costs are higher for fair trade chocolate). The farmers receive eight times more from a fair trade chocolate bar than from a typical chocolate bar. This is partly because they are paid a higher price for each kilogram of cocoa but also because fair trade chocolate bars tend to contain a higher proportion of cocoa solids. Note that 17.5 per cent VAT is added to the cost of the bar to get the retail price. Working backwards means that only 15 per cent of the retail price goes towards VAT: cost x 117.5/100 = retail price, hence retail price x 100/117.5 = cost and 100/117.5 = 85 (approximately). Therefore VAT = 15 per cent of retail price.

Solutions

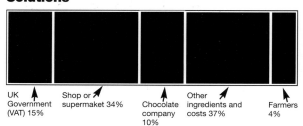

UK Government (VAT) 15%   Shop or supermaket 34%   Chocolate company 10%   Other ingredients and costs 37%   Farmers 4%

Variations

You could display the information using a pie chart or other diagram. How much do the students spend a year on chocolate? Where does that money go?

Research into different products and compare where the money goes for fair trade and other varieties. Represent this information using statistical diagrams.

Photocopy original © Amnesty International UK

ACTIVITY 19 Fair trade chocolate

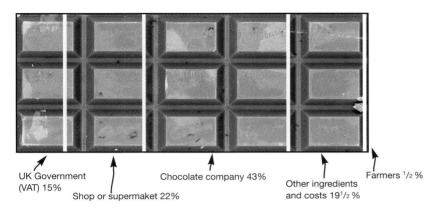

UK Government (VAT) 15%

Shop or supermaket 22%

Chocolate company 43%

Other ingredients and costs 19½ %

Farmers ½ %

A typical chocolate bar: where the money goes.

FAIRTRADE

Guarantees a **better deal** for Third World Producers

In the UK, an average person spends £62 a year on chocolate. That's the equivalent of about 200 chocolate bars. But how much of what we pay for a bar of chocolate goes to the farmers who grow the cocoa beans? You will see on the picture above that out of every £1 spent on a typical bar of chocolate containing 20 per cent cocoa, the farmer selling his or her cocoa under normal conditions gets 0.5p.

If you buy a fair trade chocolate bar, a larger proportion of what you pay goes to the farmers who grow the cocoa. Fair trade products carry the Fairtrade mark, which shows that the producers in developing countries are guaranteed better prices. The figures below show where the money goes for a Green & Black's Maya Gold fair trade chocolate bar containing 55 per cent cocoa.

UK government (VAT)	15%
Shop or supermarket	34%
Fair trade company	10%
Other ingredients and costs	37%
Farmers	4%

• Draw a diagram to represent this data.
• Compare the diagrams for a typical chocolate bar and the fair trade chocolate bar.
• Find the prices of some typical and some fair trade chocolate bars in your local shop or supermarket.
• Calculate how much of the price you pay for each bar goes to the UK government, shop or supermarket, fair trade or chocolate company and the farmers.

Ecuador - Child with cocoa beans

ACTIVITY 19 Fair trade information sheet

What is fair trade?

Many products that we eat and drink in the UK are grown by farmers in the developing world. Because of the unfair nature of world trade, these farmers often live in extreme poverty. 'Fair trade' is an alternative way of trading, which ensures that farmers are paid a fair price for their product. This helps them to improve their living conditions and those of their families and communities. Fair trade products are becoming more common in shops and supermarkets. The most common fair trade products are coffee, tea, cocoa, chocolate, bananas, sugar, honey, fruit juice and snack bars.

Coffee and cocoa trades

Most coffee and cocoa is grown by small farmers in developing countries such as Brazil, Colombia, Vietnam (coffee), Côte d'Ivoire, Ghana, Indonesia (cocoa). Farmers must make large investments of time and money when planting coffee and cocoa bushes. They often have to borrow money until their harvest is ready. In order to pay off their debts, they are forced to sell their beans as soon as they are picked, when prices are lowest. They are often taken advantage of by local traders, who buy their crop at even lower prices (as little as 50 per cent of the market price) and then sell it on at the full price. One of the biggest problems facing farmers is the rise and fall of the price of coffee and cocoa on the world market. It is common for the prices to fall so low that the money that farmers earn from selling their beans is less than the cost of growing them. This can lead to farmers falling further into debt and sometimes having to sell their land as a result.

Fair trade coffee

Fair trade coffee companies pay farmers a guaranteed minimum price for their coffee, which means that the money they earn from selling the coffee beans will always be more than the cost of growing them. Farmers are also paid an additional 10 per cent on top of the world market price. This so-called 'social premium' is used for community projects such as providing safe drinking water and sanitation, and building local schools. Fair trade companies also give farmers longer term trading agreements that help them to plan ahead. Some of the money is paid in advance, so farmers do not have to borrow money to plant coffee bushes.

Fair trade chocolate

Cocoa is one of the ingredients used for making chocolate. Other ingredients are milk, sugar and vegetable fat. A typical bar of chocolate contains only 20 per cent cocoa, whereas fair trade chocolate contains a higher percentage of cocoa, which ensures that a higher proportion of what you pay goes to the cocoa farmers. As with fair trade coffee, farmers receive a guaranteed minimum price and an additional social premium for their cocoa. Fair trade chocolate companies deal directly with farmers through co-operatives. These are businesses that are owned and run by farmers themselves, to avoid being exploited by local traders.

Useful websites

• Fairtrade Foundation at <u>www.fairtrade.org.uk</u>

© www.fairtrade.org.uk/suppliers_growers_coffee_edgar.htm

Edgar is a coffee farmer from Costa Rica. He is married, with 7 children, and is 57 years old. 'I wanted my children to have an education so that they could choose what they want to do.'

Guarantees a **better deal** for Third World Producers

ACTIVITY 20 Gender images

Attainment target and levels

England	Handling Data	4 - 6
Northern Ireland	Handling Data	3 - 6
Scotland	Information Handling	E onwards
Wales	Handling Data	4 - 6

UDHR Article 1: We are all born free and equal.

UDHR Article 2: These rights belong to everybody, whatever our differences.

Universal Declaration of Human Rights 1948

Learning objectives

• Collecting, analysing and interpreting data on gender images appearing in a resource.

• Raising awareness of stereotyping in educational resources.

• Target age range: 11-13 years.

Resources

• One copy of the Gender images activity (page 56) for each student or group of students.

• Visual or textual educational resources containing many male and female images/descriptions.

Description of activity

Students look through selected educational resources and collect references to men/women, boys/girls. They analyse and interpret the data, using tables, bar charts and pie charts.

Ensure that students have chosen a resource containing sufficient male and female images. If there are too many images, students could choose one chapter or section to analyse. The images do not necessarily need to be pictures, but could be references or written examples. Make sure that students understand the meaning of 'stereotype' and what they are expected to record in the 'occupation' and 'activity' columns of the table. Before analysing their results, students may need to group their occupations into broader categories. They may need help in classifying activities as either 'active' or 'passive'.

You could use the final question on the activity sheet as the focus for a plenary discussion. It could be argued that male/female images, rather than stereotyping, merely reflect the situation in real life.

Solutions

Research suggests that images in school textbooks tend to portray women and girls in stereotypical 'passive' roles. There tends to be a greater number of male images than female images, particularly in subjects that are considered to be more 'masculine'. Where women or girls are mentioned, they are less likely to be named than are men or boys.

Variations

Students could compare images in resources taken from different subjects, different years or different countries. They could also analyse images appearing in newspapers or other media.

You could also ask students to use the same means to investigate whether and how other groups of people are stereotyped (for example, black people and disabled people).

Useful websites

• Equal Opportunities Commission at www.eoc.org.uk provides useful statistics. Students may wish to compare their results with these.

Teachers' notes

ACTIVITY 20 Gender images

You will find many resources in your school containing what are called 'stereotypes'. These include images showing men and women in traditional roles. For example, it is a stereotype to show all doctors as male and all nurses as female.

Choose a book or other resource from your library. Look through it for references to men/boys and women/girls. See if you can find references in both pictures and written text. Then record these images in a table as in the example below.

Advert used in Equal Opportunities Commission's *What's stopping you?* campaign, November 2001. A young woman is superimposed on an image of Bobby Moore holding up the World Cup in 1966.

Image/ page number	Occupation	Gender	Name	Activity
40	doctor	male	Dr. Ahmed	performing operation
41	patient	female	none	unconscious
42	nurse	female	none	observing
43	shopper	male	Kieran	buying a book

• What proportion of all the images you have found are male/female?
• For each occupation, what proportion of images are male/female?
• What proportion of male/female images are given names?
• What proportion of male/female images play an active role?
• Represent your answers to the above, using bar charts and pie charts.
• To what extent does the resource you have chosen show stereotypes?

Advert used in Equal Opportunities Commission's What's stopping you? campaign, November 2001, using a still from the film *Billy Elliott*.

ACTIVITY 21 World literacy

Attainment target and levels

England	Handling Data	4 - 6
Northern Ireland	Handling Data	5
Scotland	Information Handling	E onwards
Wales	Handling Data	4 - 6

UDHR Article 28: There must be political order and stability so that we can all enjoy rights and freedom.

UDHR Article 26: Education is a right and primary school should be free.

Universal Declaration of Human Rights 1948

Learning objectives
• Collecting data from a secondary source, calculating the mean, drawing and interpreting multiple bar charts.
• Comparing adult literacy rates of countries in different regions of the world.
• Target age range: 11-13 years.

Resources
For each student or group of students:
• One copy of the World literacy activity (page 58).
• Spreadsheet or graph paper
• Copies of world development statistics (see Appendix 1, page 77) or access to data from an alternative source, such as the Internet.

Description of activity
Students compare and discuss adult literacy rates in different countries. Students need to be familiar with the calculation of the arithmetic mean.

It is useful to discuss the bar chart on the resource sheet with the whole class. Ask students what the largest and smallest values are for overall, female and male adult literacy. You could also ask for the ranges. Encourage students to compare the overall adult literacy rates and also the inequality in adult literacy between men and women in each country.

The bar chart shows that adult literacy rates vary from one country to another in Oceania and the range of overall adult literacy rates is 36 per cent. In general, adult literacy is higher for males than for females, the difference being greatest in Papua New Guinea.

Moving on to subsequent questions on the activity sheet, students will find overall, female and male adult literacy rates for each country in Appendix 1 or on the Internet. Ask them to investigate the range of literacy levels for the countries/regions they have chosen, using a spreadsheet to record the results, then calculate the mean and draw a bar chart.

Sharing groups' results provides a focus for a valuable plenary discussion. Are there regions where the overall literacy rate is generally higher? Are there regions where inequality between male and female adult literacy is generally larger? Are there any individual countries that do not follow the general trend?

Variations
The mean value of the adult literacy rates of countries in each region gives a 'typical' value for that region. However, it is not the same as the mean adult literacy rate for that region, as the population of every country in the region must be taken into account. Students could use a spreadsheet to find a more accurate figure for the mean adult literacy rate in each region.

Students could compare overall, female and male values of a different development indicator, such as life expectancy, school enrolment or infant mortality, for countries in different regions. They could usefully develop scatter graphs to compare literacy levels with GDP to see if the poverty of a country is related to literacy levels.

Useful websites
• United Nations Development Programme at www.undp.org. Navigate to the latest Human Development Report, then to Human Development Indicators. (It can be a useful to make a back-up copy of the relevant web pages in case of problems with Internet access during the lesson.)

Teachers' notes

ACTIVITY 21 World literacy

The adult literacy rate of a country is the percentage of its people aged 15 or over who are able to read and write a simple sentence.

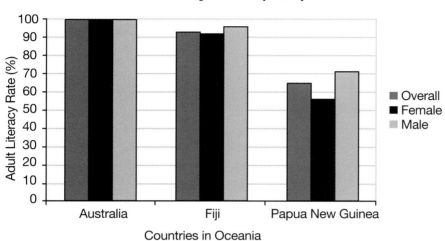

Adult Literacy Rates (1997)

The bar chart above shows the adult literacy rates for three countries in Oceania.

The mean of the overall adult literacy rates is (100 + 93 + 64) ÷ 3 = 86%

The mean of the female adult literacy rates is (100 + 91 + 56) ÷ 3 = 82%

The mean of the male adult literacy rates is (100 + 95 + 71) ÷ 3 = 89%

• What do these results tell you about adult literacy in Oceania?

Choose two or more regions from the following: Africa, Asia & Middle East, Europe, Latin America & Caribbean, North America.
• Find the overall, female and male adult literacy rates for a selection of countries in each region.
• Represent the adult literacy rates for each region in a bar chart.
• Calculate the mean of the adult literacy rates for the countries in each region.
• What do your results tell you about adult literacy in your chosen regions?

© *Image by Julie Eagles, courtesy of Oxfam Australia*

Students in class at the Sipuru village community school, Papua New Guinea

ACTIVITY 22 Average wages

Attainment target and levels

England	Handling Data	5 - 6
Northern Ireland	Handling Data	5 - 7
Scotland	Information Handling	F and credit
Wales	Handling Data	5 - 6

UDHR Article 23: Every adult has the right to a job, to a fair wage for their work and to join a trade union and choose what work they do.

Universal Declaration of Human Rights 1948

Learning objectives

• Calculating the mean, median and mode and deciding which is the most appropriate measure of average in a given context.
• Appreciating how different groups may use a different measure of average to suit their own interests.
• Target age range: 12-14 years.

Resources

• One copy of the Average wages activity (page 60) for each student or group of students.
• Copies of job advertisements from a newspaper or the Internet (optional).

Description of activity

The activity looks at wages paid to workers in two cafes: the Red Herring and Chicken King. Students are asked to identify which employer pays the higher average wage and to explore which form of average (mean, median or mode) is the fairest to apply.

Students should have experience of calculating mean, median, mode and range of discrete data before attempting this work. Try writing the definitions on the board to avoid confusion.

A plenary discussion could explore how different measures of average can be used to support different, and possibly contradictory, hypotheses. For example, the lowest paid workers at Chicken King might use the median wage to justify why they should have a pay rise. The manager might use the mean to argue that the workers are already better off than workers elsewhere. The mean tends to be distorted by one or two extreme values.

In real life, the World Bank and International Monetary Fund (IMF) use Gross National Product (GNP) or Gross Domestic Product (GDP) per capita (the mean income) to compare the wealth of different countries. In the United Kingdom, the Trades Union Congress (TUC) supports a minimum wage of half male median earnings. Many European countries have a minimum wage based on the Council of Europe's 'decency threshold', which is defined as two-thirds of median earnings (male and female combined).

Encourage students to consider which average is the fairest to use as a measure of the average wage.

Solutions

• At the Red Herring the average wage could be any of the following:
mean = £5.66, median = £5.20, mode = £5.20.
• At Chicken King the average wage could be any of the following:
mean = £5.71, median = £4.50, mode = £3.90.
• The average wage is highest at the Red Herring if you use the median or mode.
• The average wage is highest at Chicken King if you use the mean.

Variations

The pictogram on the resource sheet illustrates inequities in the wages of workers at each workplace. Explore other ways of measuring and representing these inequities, (for example, range, cumulative frequency graph, inter-quartile range).

Present the students with another, similar problem of your own, using real job advertisements to make it more realistic. See if you and the students can come up with a situation where there are three workplaces, each with the highest average wage using one of the measures.

Photocopy original © Amnesty International UK

ACTIVITY 22 Average wages

Look at the diagrams below, which represent the wages paid to workers in two cafés: the Red Herring and Chicken King.

The workers at the Red Herring claim that their average wage is higher than that of the workers at Chicken King. But the manager of Chicken King claims that the average wage of workers there is higher than that in the Red Herring.

Use your knowledge of mean, median and mode average measures to calculate the average rates of pay in both cafés. Then answer the following questions:

• Who do you agree with?

• Justify your answer.

A fast-food employee gives a customer her order at Pleasant Grove in Utah in the USA, 1999.

The Red Herring

At the Red Herring health food café, the workers are paid at the following rates:

• The manager earns £8.30 per hour.

• There are 2 cooks who each earn £6.30 per hour.

• There are 4 assistants who each earn £5.20 per hour.

• There are 2 trainees who each earn £4.60 per hour.

Chicken King

At the Chicken King fast food outlet, the workers are paid at the following rates:

• The manager earns £11.20 per hour.

• The production manager earns £9.10 per hour.

• There are 2 supervisors who each earn £6.70 per hour.

• There are 3 senior assistants who each earn £4.50 per hour.

• There are 4 junior assistants who each earn £3.90 per hour.

ACTIVITY 23 Child labour

Attainment target and levels

England	Handling Data	5 - 6
Northern Ireland	Handling Data	5 - 6
Scotland	Information Handling	E onwards
Wales	Handling Data	5 - 6

UDHR Article 25: We all have the right to enjoy a good life. Mothers, children, the elderly, the unemployed and the disabled have the right to be cared for.

Universal Declaration of Human Rights 1948

Learning objectives

• Drawing and interpreting spreadsheets and/or pie charts.
• Comparing time spent working and on other activities, by children in the UK and the developing world.
• Target age range: 12-14 years.

Resources

• One copy of the Child labour activity (page 62) for each student or group of students.
• A pre-designed spreadsheet or template would be useful.

Description of activity

Ensure students understand how to represent a daily routine via a spreadsheet or pie chart.

Students could lay out their own routines in a similar way, which will help them to organise the data. Ask them to decide on broad categories, such as 'household chores', into which they can group parts of the routine. You may wish to discuss a suitable degree of accuracy for estimating the time spent on each activity. Students should display the percentage of the day spent on each category in their own spreadsheet.

Alternatively, you can ask students to devise a pie chart representing Anjella's routine, such as the one opposite, where activities have been grouped into broad categories ('household chores' etc). They could then construct a similar pie chart for their own daily routines.

A plenary discussion could focus on the other forms of child labour prevalent around the world.

Variations

Ask the students to look for other case studies involving child labour on the Internet, in books, newspapers, etc. They can represent these case studies by using statistical diagrams such as pie charts and then compare them with their own daily routines and that of Anjella.

Students could compare the daily routines of family members or friends in a similar way. Do they think the daily routines would be different for older/younger members of their family or for male/female friends?

They could also use compound bar charts to display data.

Anjella's Day

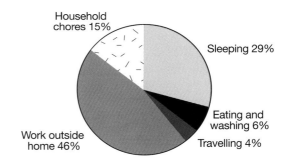

Teachers' notes

ACTIVITY 23 Child labour

Many children around the world have to work to help support their families.

Anjella is 12 years old and lives in Kenya. She does not attend school because her family can't afford the fees and they rely on her labour in the home and on the farm. Anjella's daily routine is as follows:

Anjella's daily routine:
4.45am: Wake up, wash and eat.
5.00am: Walk to the fields.
5.30am: Work in the fields all day.
3.00pm: Help collect firewood and return home.
4.00pm: Help pound and grind corn.
5.30pm: Collect water
6.30pm: Look after brothers and sisters.
8.00pm: Eat, then help wash dishes.
9.00pm: Wash and go to bed.

• Complete the table to show how much time Anjella spends on each part of her routine.
• Create a pie chart to show her routine, grouping some of the activities into broad categories (for example, 'household chores').
• Write down your daily routine for a typical school day.
• Construct a table for your own daily routine.
• Draw a pie chart to represent your day, grouping your activities into broad categories.
• Compare your daily routine to Anjella's daily routine.

© Bernard Muthaka, 2003/Courtesy of Photoshare, www.photoshare.org

Hellen Akoth, a 10-year-old girl from Western Kenya, walks a kilometre to find cooking charcoal. When she returns home, she will prepare a meal for her family of seven, including three boys who go to school. Girls in Kenya enter into their stereotyped roles early in life. Most cannot go to school as their parents want them to assist with house chores. Those who go to school have to balance the two.

Activity	Start time	End time	Duration
Wake up, wash & eat			
Walk to fields			
Work in fields			
Collect firewood			
Pound & grind corn			
Collect water			
Look after siblings			
Eat & wash up			
Wash & go to bed			
Sleeping			
Total time (hours)			**24**

ACTIVITY 24 Duties survey

Attainment target and levels

England	Handling Data	5 - 6
Northern Ireland	Handling Data	5 - 6
Scotland	Information Handling	E onwards
Wales	Handling Data	5 - 6

UDHR Article 29: We all have a duty to other people and we should protect their rights and freedom.

Universal Declaration of Human Rights 1948

Learning objectives
• Collecting data using a tally chart, making calculations using percentages, drawing and interpreting statistical diagrams.
• Carrying out a survey of what people consider duties to their community.
• Target age range: 12-14 years.

Resources
• One copy of the Duties survey activity (page 64) for each student or group of students.
• Spreadsheet (optional).

Description of activity
Discuss what is meant by a 'duty' to the community. Emphasise that 'duty' means more than 'obligation' and 'the right thing to do'. Encourage students to think of some actions and activities that most people would consider as duties, and others that they would not. Agree a list of actions for all the students to incorporate into a survey. They will need to think carefully about (and agree on) the wording for each one so as to avoid asking leading questions. In order to produce a final survey of significant size, it is best if students all ask the same questions. Discuss with them what they consider to be an appropriate sample size for each of them to obtain, also how they can make the sample representative of their community.

Collecting the data is a good homework task. Students should check that their percentage calculations for each activity total 100 per cent when added together. Appropriate statistical diagrams to use are a multiple bar chart, a compound bar chart (representing all results) or a series of pie charts (each representing one activity).

A plenary discussion could focus on groups of students sharing the findings from their survey with the rest of the class. Ask them to comment on whether the findings were what they expected before carrying out the survey. Then compile all the results to produce a sample of significant size, using if possible a database to record the results.

Variations
Students could carry out a similar survey using other categories instead of 'duties'. These could include, for example, actions that people consider as 'rights' or 'responsibilities', or specific 'government policies' and whether or not people agree with them.

Teachers' notes

ACTIVITY 24 Duties survey

Your task is to carry out a survey of activities that people might regard as duties to their community! First of all, think up your own set of possible duties. Your data collection sheet might look similar to the one below.

• Decide how many people you will ask and approach them with your data collection sheet.

• Record each person's responses in the correct column using a tally.

• For each activity, write down the frequency of each response and convert this frequency into a percentage.

• Represent your results using statistical diagrams.

• Summarise what you have found out from your survey.

Student reading Rights of the Child poster at Amnesty International Youth Conference 2004

Sample data collection sheet

It is your duty to ...	Agree (tally)	Can't decide (tally)	Disagree (tally)
...put litter in the litter bin.			
...report a friend you know has broken the law.			
...give money to charity.			
...take used bottles and cans to the recycling centre.			
...vote in elections when you are old enough.			
...look after your elderly relatives.			
...tell a shop cashier if they give you too much change.			
...hand in money you find in the street.			

Students demonstrate in the Stop Violence Against Women campaign. Amnesty International Youth Conference 2004.

ACTIVITY 25 Refugees

Attainment target and levels

England	Handling Data	5 - 7
Northern Ireland	Handling Data	5 - 7
Scotland	Information Handling	F and Credit
Wales	Handling Data	5 - 7

UDHR Article 14: If we are frightened or badly treated in our own country, we all have the right to emigrate to another country for our own safety.

Universal Declaration of Human Rights 1948

Learning objectives

• Drawing and interpreting appropriate statistical diagrams to represent a set of data.
• Appreciating the situation of refugees in the UK and worldwide through analysing relevant data.
• Target age range: 12-14 years.

Resources

• One copy of the Refugees activity (page 66) for each student or group of students.
• Spreadsheet or graph paper.

Description of activity

Students are asked to draw statistical diagrams to represent data on refugees and asylum seekers. Students should work in groups and focus on one aspect of the data (for example, one group could concentrate solely on the issue of asylum seekers). The work carried out by the different groups could then contribute to an overall project on refugees.

You may wish to start by discussing which statistical diagrams might be appropriate for each table and why. Appropriate calculations could be used to generate other useful data – for example, for Table 2 you could calculate the number of refugees per 1,000 population in each country, for Table 3 you could calculate the percentage of successful asylum applications in each year. Note that in Table 3, 'successful applications' include those to whom refugee status is granted and those who are given exceptional leave to remain. It does not include those whose appeal against an unsuccessful initial application is upheld.

A plenary discussion could be used to give a broader picture of the plight of refugees than that offered by the statistics alone. This activity is ideal for generating a thought-provoking classroom display.

Solutions

You could use some or all of the following statistical diagrams to represent the data:

Table 1 – two-way table with percentages, compound bar chart, pie charts.
Table 2 – bar chart, multiple bar chart, scatter graph.
Table 3 – compound bar chart, line graph.

Variations

Students could carry out further statistical research into refugees using the websites mentioned below as starting points. They could investigate more recent statistics to see if the same patterns have continued. Alternatively, you could download further statistics from these websites for students to analyse.

Groups of students could take it in turns to present their results to the rest of the class.

Useful websites

• United Nations High Commissioner for Refugees at www.unhcr.ch
• Refugee Council at www.refugeecouncil.org.uk.

ACTIVITY 25 Refugees

The United Nations High Commission for Refugees (UNHCR) provides assistance to the following groups of people (called 'persons of concern'):

Refugees are those who have been forced to leave their country and are unable to return because of war or fear of persecution. They might be persecuted for their race, religion, nationality, social group or political views. Refugees have the right to be protected under international law.

Asylum seekers are those who have been forced to leave their country and who apply to be recognised as refugees in another country.

Internally displaced persons (IDPs) are those who have been forced to leave their homes but remain in their country of origin.

Returned refugees are former refugees who return to their country.

The tables below illustrate the situation of refugees and others of concern to the UNHCR in the UK and worldwide.

• Represent the information in the tables using statistical diagrams. You could draw bar charts, pie charts, line graphs, etc.

• What do your diagrams show?

Table 1: Persons of concern to the UNHCR (January 2000)

Region	Refugees	Asylum seekers	Returned refugees	IDPs and others	Total
Africa	3,523,250	61,110	933,890	1,732,290	6,250,540
Asia	4,781,750	24,750	617,620	1,884,740	7,308,860
Europe	2,608,380	473,060	952,060	3,252,300	7,285,800
Latin America & Carib.	61,200	1,510	6,260	21,200	90,170
North America	636,300	605,630	-	-	1,241,930
Oceania	64,500	15,540	-	-	80,040
Total	11,675,380	1,181,600	2,509,830	6,890,530	22,257,340

Table 2: Comparison of population of concern and population of country (1999)

Country of *asylum*	Population of concern	Population of country
China	290,000	1264,800,000
Germany	1,240,000	82,000,000
Guinea	540,000	8,000,000
Iran	880,000	69,200,000
Pakistan	1,060,000	137,600,000
Sudan	400,000	30,400,000
Tanzania	650,000	34,300,000
United States	1,100,000	280,400,000
Yugoslavia	1,650,000	10,600,000

Table 3: *Asylum* applications in the UK (1985-2001)

Year	1985	1986	1987	1988	1989	1990	1991	1992	1993
New	5,444	4,266	4,256	3,998	11,640	26,205	44,840	24,605	22,370
Successful	2,987	2,450	1,797	2,206	6,070	3,320	2,695	16,440	12,715

Year	1994	1995	1996	1997	1998	1999	2000	2001	
New	32,830	43,965	29,640	32,500	46,010	71,160	80,315	71,700	
Successful	4,485	5,705	7,295	7,100	9,255	10,280	21,870	30,470	

Photocopy original © Amnesty International UK

ACTIVITY 26 Fair trade coffee

Attainment target and levels

England	Handling Data	5 - 7
Northern Ireland	Handling Data	6 - 7
Scotland	Information Handling	E onwards
Wales	Handling Data	5 - 7

UDHR Article 23: Every adult has the right to a job, to a fair wage for their work and to join a trade union and choose what work they do.

Universal Declaration of Human Rights 1948

Learning objectives

• Drawing and interpreting line graphs involving a 15-year span of time and calculating using percentages.

• Comparing the price paid to growers by fair trade and other companies.

• Target age range: 12-14 years.

Resources

• One copy of the Fair trade coffee activity (page 68) and information sheet (page 54) for each student or group of students.

• Graph paper or spreadsheet.

Description of activity

Students analyse a graph showing the world market price of coffee between 1985 and 2000. They then calculate the fair trade price paid to growers in Latin America over that period and draw a graph showing both prices. In order to compare the graphs for fair trade price and world market price it is useful to plot them on the same axes. You will need to ensure that the students use an appropriate scale.

Use the information sheet (page 54) as a focus for an introductory discussion with students in order to gain a fuller understanding of fair trade.

Ensure students are able to read off the values from the vertical scale. You could check this by asking students for the maximum and minimum prices and the range. You could get students to draw their graphs either on graph paper or by using a spreadsheet.

A plenary discussion could focus on how the fair trade price is not only higher, but also shows

less fluctuation, allowing farmers to plan ahead. The guaranteed minimum price means that farmers will always make a profit from their crop. In reality, the benefit of the fair trade price to farmers is even greater than shown on the graph (see information sheet).

Solutions

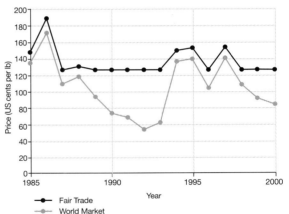

World Market/Fair Trade Prices of Coffee

Variations

Find the retail price for a fairly traded and other jar of instant coffee. Using the fact that 300g of coffee beans are needed to make 100g of instant coffee, calculate the percentage of the retail price that would have been paid to farmers for each product in various years.

ACTIVITY 26 Fair trade coffee

WHAT'S THAT IN YOUR COFFEE?

Poverty and misery for coffee growers, massive profits for big coffee companies.
If you love coffee but find this hard to swallow, join us now and demand
a decent price for poor farmers.

www.maketradefair.com

MAKE TRADE FAIR   Oxfam

Most coffee is grown on small farms in Latin America, Asia and Africa. One of the biggest problems for the farmers is the rise and fall of the price of coffee on the world market – see the graph.

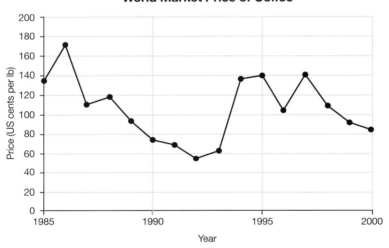

Fair trade coffee, such as 'Cafédirect', helps the farmers by paying them a fair price for the coffee they grow. The farmers are paid 10 per cent more than the market price (this is called the 'social premium'). There is also a guaranteed minimum fair trade price. Growers in Latin America, for example, are never paid less than 126 US cents per lb.

• Use the graph to find the world market price of coffee for each year between 1985 and 2000.
• Calculate the fair trade price paid to growers in Latin America for each year.
• Draw a graph showing both the world market price of coffee and the fair trade price paid to growers in Latin America between 1985 and 2000.
• Comment on your graph.

Coffee beans harvested by a woman named Florence Lwango in the Luweero District of Uganda. She hopes to sell them at market. Lwango is the guardian of eight grandchildren who were orphaned due to the death of her two sons from AIDS.

ACTIVITY 27 Population change

Attainment target and levels

England	Handling Data	5 - 7
Northern Ireland	Handling Data	5 - 7
Scotland	Information Handling	E onwards
Wales	Handling Data	5 - 7

UDHR Article 2: These rights belong to everybody, whatever our differences.

Universal Declaration of Human Rights 1948

Learning objectives

• Drawing and interpreting bar charts and pie charts and calculating using percentages.
• Comparing projected population growth for different regions of the world.
• Target age range: 13-15 years.

Resources

• One copy of the Population Change activity (page 70) for each student or group of students.
• Peters Projection world map (page 38).

Description of activity

Ensure students understand how to calculate the population of each region in 2001 and 2050 (particularly how to deal with the negative growth rate).

A plenary discussion could focus on interpreting the three statistical diagrams. Emphasise that, although Africa has the largest population growth, it will still have a smaller population than Asia in 2050 but will have overtaken Europe. Ask students for the projected population growth for the whole world and discuss why this is not the same as the mean of the projected population growths of the regions. Discuss reasons why some regions have a higher growth rate: for example, parents in poorer countries often have more children to ensure that some will survive to support them in old age (they may have little access to health care and a higher prevalence of life-threatening diseases).

Solutions

The projected population growth for the whole world between 2001 and 2050 is 49 per cent.

Projected Population (2050)

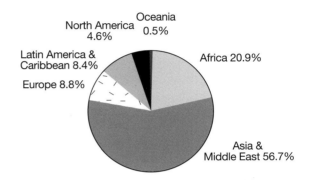

Variations

Carry out further research into world population growth and find other ways of representing your data, such as multiple bar charts and line graphs. You could ask students to use the same techniques to investigate and represent related information, such as the increasing prevalence of HIV and AIDS in developing countries.

Use the Peters Projection map of the world to find the area of each region; then calculate and compare the population densities of each region in 2001 and 2050.

Useful websites

• United Nations Population Fund at www.unfpa.org

ACTIVITY 27 Population change

The pie chart below shows the proportion of the world's population in different regions of the world in 2001. The total world population in 2001 was 6,418 million. More than a billion people are between the ages of 15 and 24. Among young girls aged 15 to 19, 15 million give birth each year. The bar chart below represents the predicted population increase between 2001 and 2050 for each region.

- Calculate the population of each region in 2001.
- Calculate the predicted population of each region in 2050.
- Represent your results for 2050 in a pie chart.
- Calculate the projected population growth for the whole world between 2001 and 2050.
- Use the diagrams to compare the populations of different regions in the world in 2001 and 2050.

© Patrick Coleman/CCP/Courtesy of Photoshare, www.photoshare.org

High school students attend a DramAidE forum theatre performance at a high school in Kwazulu Natal, a province in South Africa with the highest HIV/AIDS prevalence. (Spring 2000)

Projected Population (2001)

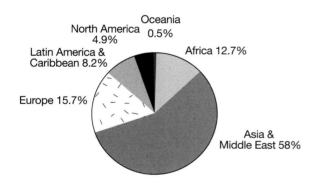

North America 4.9%
Oceania 0.5%
Africa 12.7%
Latin America & Caribbean 8.2%
Europe 15.7%
Asia & Middle East 58%

Projected Population Growth (2001 to 2050)

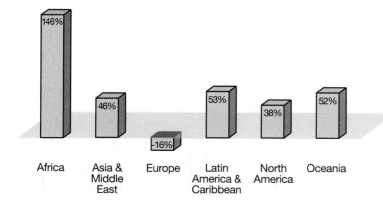

Africa 146%
Asia & Middle East 46%
Europe -16%
Latin America & Caribbean 53%
North America 38%
Oceania 52%

ACTIVITY 28 Attitudes survey

Attainment target and levels

England	Handling Data	5 - 7
Northern Ireland	Handling Data	5 - 7
Scotland	Information Handling	F and Credit
Wales	Handling Data	5 - 7

UDHR Article 19: We all have the right to make up our own minds, to think what we like and say what we think, as well as to share our ideas with other people.

Universal Declaration of Human Rights 1948

Learning objectives
• Designing a questionnaire, analysing responses and presenting the results.
• Carrying out a survey into different attitudes towards current issues.
• Target age range: 13-15 years.

Resources
• One copy of the Attitudes survey activity (page 72) for each student or group of students.
• Newspapers or Internet access (optional).

Description of activity
Ask the students to devise and design a questionnaire that looks at the attitudes of different groups of people on specific issues.

Ensure that students appreciate that certain features must be included in their questionnaire to allow detailed analysis at a later stage. There should be a graded scale of numerical responses for each question, such as 5 for 'strongly agree', 4 for 'agree', 3 for 'can't decide', 2 for 'disagree', 1 for 'strongly disagree'. Enough personal information on each interviewee should be included to enable the students to compare the different groups of respondents. (So include, for example, gender, approximate age range and occupation.)

Encourage students to choose questions with which they think most people will agree and other questions with which most will disagree. They should think carefully about how to word their questions to avoid bias. Discuss how many people from each group there should be in the sample.

Carrying out this survey would be an appropriate task to set as homework.

Once the questionnaires are completed, get the students to collate the responses using a frequency table for each group. For each question, they should calculate the mean, median or mode as a measure of average and range or inter-quartile range as a measure of spread. Ask them to represent their results using one or more of the following statistical diagrams: multiple bar charts, compound bar charts, pie charts, frequency polygons, box and whisker plots. They should justify the appropriateness of each of their choices of measure of average and spread as well as statistical diagrams. They should then use their calculations and diagrams to compare the extent to which different groups agree with the questions asked.

You could instigate a plenary discussion for students to focus on sharing their findings and consider the implications (for example, girls are less likely to opt for maths at 'A' level, despite performing equally well as boys at GCSE, if they consider maths to be a boys' subject).

Variations
Compare the results of your survey with regional, national or international data available in newspapers and on the Internet.

Teachers' notes

ACTIVITY 28 Attitudes survey

Carry out a survey to compare the attitudes of different groups of people towards issues of your choice. You need to design a questionnaire which includes numerical values as responses. Your questionnaire might look similar to the one below.

• Decide how many people you will survey in each group.
• Ask each person to complete a copy of your questionnaire.
• Collate and summarise the responses to each question.
• Analyse your results by calculating measures of average and spread.
• Represent your results using appropriate statistical diagrams.
• Summarise what you have found out from your survey.

© Marie-Anne.Ventoura

Amnesty Internatonal Youth Group members in front of Control Arms banner. Amnesty International Youth Conference 2004

Do you agree that ... ?	Agree <--------------------------> Disagree				
...maths is a boys' subject.	O 5	O 4	O 3	O 2	O 1
...third World debt should be cancelled immediately.	O 5	O 4	O 3	O 2	O 1
...parents should not be allowed to smack their children.	O 5	O 4	O 3	O 2	O 1
...capital punishment should be abolished throughout the world.	O 5	O 4	O 3	O 2	O 1
Personal information					
Gender	O male	O female			
Age	O 11-14	O 15-18	O 19-22	O 23+	
Occupation	O student	O teacher	O parent		

© Marie-Anne Ventoura

Kierra Box, 19, speaks at the Amnesty International Youth Conference 2004. She is from the 'Hands up for...' campaign, which is run by young people to encourage political participation, democracy and debate throughout society.

ACTIVITY 29 Development indicators

Attainment target and levels

England	Handling Data	6 - 7
Northern Ireland	Handling Data	6 - 7
Scotland	Information Handling	F onwards
Wales	Handling Data	6 - 7

UDHR Article 22: We all have the right to a home, enough money to live on and medical help if we are ill. Music, art, craft and sport should be for everyone to enjoy.

Universal Declaration of Human Rights 1948

Learning objectives

• Drawing scatter graphs and using these to describe the correlation between two variables.
• Exploring the relations between different development indicators.
• Target age range: 13-15 years.

Resources

• One copy of the Development indicators activity (page 74), World development statistics (page 77) or Internet access for each student or group of students.
• Spreadsheet (optional).

Description of activity

Start by discussing with students what is meant by positive and negative correlation using the scatter graphs on the resource sheet as examples. Students can refer to the World development statistics in Appendix 1 or use the Internet to collect the necessary data.

Encourage the students to choose countries from a wide range of geographical regions. They should record their results on a spreadsheet, which will help them to see further correlations between pairs of development indicators. Ensure that students understand the definition of all development indicators shown on the resource sheet.

A plenary discussion will encourage students to focus on any correlations between different development indicators and decide whether or not these are 'causal' relations. For example, the positive correlation between secondary enrolment and adult literacy is causal because attending school leads directly to improving literacy. However, the negative correlation between adult literacy and infant

mortality is not causal because higher adult literacy is a consequence of better education provision whereas lower infant mortality is a consequence of better health provision.

Try discussing other ways in which students could use a scatter graph. For example, drawing a line of best fit for the first scatter graph would help them to predict the infant mortality rate if they knew a country's life expectancy.

Solutions

• Life expectancy and infant mortality have a negative correlation, which is causal (infant mortality affects life expectancy).
• Secondary enrolment and adult literacy have a positive correlation, which is causal (see above).
• Adult literacy and infant mortality have a negative correlation (non-causal).
• Population and infant mortality have no correlation.
• GDP per capita and secondary enrolment have a positive correlation, which is causal. (This is due to the effect on secondary enrolment of GDP per capita, as wealthier families can afford the secondary school fees that are commonly charged in developing countries.)

Variations

Explore other ways of demonstrating a correlation between different development indicators. You could divide countries into groups according to one indicator and calculate the mean value of the other indicator for each group. A steady increase or decrease in these values would suggest a correlation.

Useful websites

• United Nations Development Programme at www.undp.org (navigate to the latest Human Development Report, then human development indicators).

ACTIVITY 29 Development indicators

A 'development indicator' is a measure that can be used to show the relative wellbeing of the population of a country. Two examples of development indicators are a country's life expectancy and infant mortality.

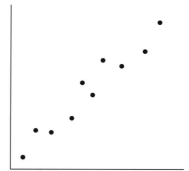

This scatter graph shows a positive correlation.

• Draw a scatter graph of life expectancy and infant mortality for a range of countries from around the world.
• Does your graph show a positive correlation, a negative correlation or no correlation at all?
• Explain in your own words what this means.

Which type of correlation would you expect to find if you drew a scatter graph of:
• secondary enrolment and adult literacy?
• adult literacy and infant mortality?
• population and life expectancy?
• secondary enrolment and GDP per capita?

Find the type of correlation between these or other pairs of development indicators by drawing scatter graphs.

This scatter graph shows a negative correlation.

Huang Bohao, 86, left, Huang Yinlong, 88, centre, and Huang Boliao, 89, play Chinese chess using a carved rock for a playing surface, and stones and pieces of corn as pieces, at their village in Bama County, in China's southern Guangxi province. The three are relative youngsters by the standards of the county, which is famous in China for its large numbers of elderly residents, many in their 90s and 100s.

ACTIVITY 30 Global inequality

Attainment target and levels

England	Handling Data	6 - 7
Northern Ireland	Handling Data	7
Scotland	Information Handling	Not part of curriculum but may be possible for more able pupils.
Wales	Handling Data	6 - 7

UDHR Article 2: These rights belong to everybody, whatever our differences.

Universal Declaration of Human Rights 1948

Learning objectives
• Drawing and interpreting statistical diagrams involving representation by area, such as the Lorenz Curve.
• Exploring the inequality in incomes of the world's population.
• Target age range: 13-15 years.

Resources
• One copy of the Global inequality activity (page 76) for each student or group of students
• Graph paper
• Internet access (optional).

Description of activity
You might like to introduce the activity by discussing the initial statement on the activity sheet: 'Global inequality doubled between 1965 and 1990.' Ask the students to consider ways of measuring the inequalities shown in the table. The ratio of income of the richest 20 per cent (quintile) divided by income of the poorest 20 per cent has roughly doubled between 1965 and 1990. Using this as a measure of inequality demonstrates that the statement is true.

Ensure students understand how the Lorenz curve has been drawn. You could get them to recreate the curve on graph paper in order to calculate the Gini Coefficient. Do this either by counting squares or by approximating with a series of triangles or trapezia.

A plenary discussion could focus on the limitations of different measures of inequality. For example, GDP (on which the income of each population quintile is based) is measured in US dollars and fails to take into account the purchasing power within different countries.

Solutions
The Gini Coefficients for world income in 1970, 1980 and 1989 were 0.71, 0.79 and 0.87 respectively.

Variations
Draw a Lorenz curve for the income of the world's population in 1965, 1970, 1980 and 1990. You could first draw a series of trapezia with appropriate areas before drawing the curves.

Explore measures of inequality within individual countries by, for example, using the Gini Coefficient or comparing the richest/poorest 10 or 20 per cent.

Useful websites
• United Nations Development Programme at www.undp.org (navigate to the latest Human Development Report, then human development indicators.)

ACTIVITY 30 Global inequality

- 'Global inequality doubled between 1965 and 1990.' Do you think this statement is true?
- Use the table below to justify your answer.

Another way of measuring inequality is the Gini Coefficient. To calculate this, first draw a Lorenz curve, as below. The Gini Coefficient is the ratio of the area between the curve and the diagonal line divided by the area of the triangle below the diagonal. The Gini Coefficient varies between 0 (perfect equality) and 1 (extreme inequality).

- Investigate the change in global inequality using the Gini Coefficient.

Lorenz Curve for Global Inequality (1989)

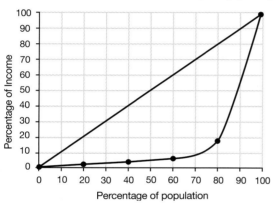

Share of the World's Income (1989)

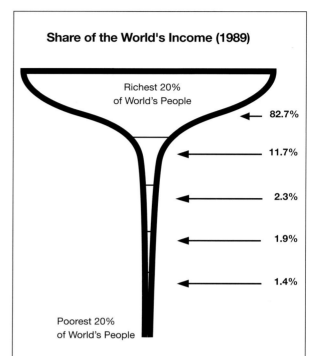

Richest 20% of World's People

82.7%

11.7%

2.3%

1.9%

1.4%

Poorest 20% of World's People

The UNDP's *Human Development Report* (1992) focused on the inequality in people's incomes in different countries around the world. This diagram (based on data from 1989) is taken from the report.

Income of Groups (each 20% of the world's population)

Year	Poorest 20%	Second 20%	Third 20%	Fourth 20%	Richest 20%
1965	2.3	2.9	4.2	21.2	69.5
1970	2.2	2.8	3.9	21.3	70.0
1980	1.7	2.2	3.5	18.3	75.4
1990	1.4	1.8	2.1	11.3	83.4

Scavenging to make a living on a town dump, Philippines, 1990.

Photocopy original © Amnesty International UK

© Maillard J.

Appendix 1: World development statistics

Country	Region	Life expectancy (2002)	Infant mortality per 1,000 births (2002)	Adult literacy (%) (2001)	Female adult literacy (2001 or latest available)	Male adult literacy (2001 or latest available)	Secondary school enrolment (2001)	GDP per capita in US dollars (2001) at purchasing power parity	Population in millions (2002)
Afghanistan	Asia/ME	43	165	36	21	51	–	*700	22.9
Albania	Europe	74	26	85	78	93	74	3,680	3.1
Algeria	Africa	70	39	68	58	77	62	6,090	31.2
Angola	Africa	40	154	42	–	–	–	2,040	13.2
Argentina	Lat/Car	74	16	97	97	97	79	11,320	38.0
Armenia	Asia/ME	72	30	98	98	99	64	2,650	3.1
Australia	Oceania	79	6	–	–	–	90	25,370	19.6
Austria	Europe	78	5	–	–	–	89	26,730	8.1
Azerbaijan	Asia/ME	72	74	97	96	99	78	3,090	8.3
Bahamas	Lat/Car	67	13	96	96	95	72	16,270	0.3
Bahrain	Asia/ME	74	13	88	83	91	92	16,060	0.7
Bangladesh	Asia/ME	61	51	41	31	50	43	1,610	143.8
Barbados	Lat/Car	77	12	100	100	100	85	15,560	0.3
Belarus	Europe	70	17	100	100	100	76	7,620	9.9
Belgium	Europe	79	5	–	–	–	–	25,520	10.3
Belize	Lat/Car	72	34	93	93	94	63	5,690	0.3
Benin	Africa	51	93	39	25	54	17	980	6.6
Bhutan	Asia/ME	63	74	47	34	61	–	1,833	2.2
Bolivia	Lat/Car	64	56	86	80	92	68	2,300	8.6
Bosnia & Herzegovina	Europe	74	15	93	89	98	–	5,970	4.1
Botswana	Africa	41	80	78	81	75	70	7,820	1.8
Brazil	Lat/Car	68	30	87	87	87	71	7,360	176.3
Brunei Darussalam	Asia/ME	76	6	92	88	95	–	19,210	0.4
Bulgaria	Europe	71	14	99	98	99	88	6,890	8.0
Burkina Faso	Africa	46	107	25	15	35	8	1,120	12.6
Burundi	Africa	41	114	49	42	57	–	690	6.6
Cambodia	Asia/ME	57	96	69	58	81	17	1,860	13.8
Cameroon	Africa	47	95	72	65	80	–	1,680	15.7
Canada	N.Amer	79	5	–	–	–	98	27,130	31.3
Cape Verde	Africa	70	29	75	67	85	–	5,570	0.5
Central African Rep	Africa	40	115	48	37	61	–	1,300	3.8
Chad	Africa	45	117	44	36	53	8	1,070	8.3
Chile	Lat/Car	76	10	96	96	96	75	9,190	15.6
China	Asia/ME	71	31	86	79	93	–	4,020	1,294.9
Colombia	Lat/Car	72	19	92	92	92	57	7,040	43.5
Comoros	Africa	61	59	56	49	63	–	1,870	0.7
Congo	Africa	48	81	82	76	88	–	970	3.6
Congo (Dem Rep of)	Africa	41	129	63	52	74	12	680	51.2
Costa Rica	Lat/Car	78	9	96	96	96	49	9,460	4.1
Côte D'Ivoire	Africa	41	102	50	38	60	–	1,490	16.4
Croatia	Europe	74	7	98	97	99	–	9,170	4.4
Cuba	Lat/Car	77	7	97	97	97	82	5,259	11.3
Cyprus	Asia/ME	78	5	97	96	99	88	21,190	0.8
Czech Republic	Europe	75	4	–	–	–	–	14,720	10.2

*Sources: UNICEF, State of the World's Children 2004 and UNDP, Human Development Report 2003. *Estimates from CIA World Factbook*

Country	Region	Life expectancy (2002)	Infant mortality per 1,000 births (2002)	Adult literacy (%) (2001)	Female adult literacy (2001 or latest available)	Male adult literacy (2001 or latest available)	Secondary school enrolment (2001)	GDP per capita in US dollars (2001) at purchasing power parity	Population in millions (2002)
Denmark	Europe	77	4	–	–	–	89	29,000	5.4
Djibouti	Africa	46	100	66	56	76	–	2,370	0.7
Dominican Republic	Lat/Car	67	32	84	84	84	40	7,020	8.6
Ecuador	Lat/Car	71	25	92	90	93	48	3,280	12.8
Egypt	Africa	69	35	56	45	67	79	3,520	70.5
El Salvador	Lat/Car	71	33	79	77	82	39	5,260	64.2
Equatorial Guinea	Africa	49	101	84	76	93	26	15,073	0.5
Eritrea	Africa	53	47	57	46	68	22	1,030	4.0
Estonia	Europe	72	10	100	100	100	83	10,170	1.3
Ethiopia	Africa	46	114	40	32	48	13	810	69.0
Fiji	Oceania	70	17	93	91	95	–	4,850	0.8
Finland	Europe	78	4	–	–	–	95	24,430	5.2
France	Europe	79	4	–	–	–	92	23,990	59.9
Gabon	Africa	57	60	71	62	80	–	5,990	1.3
Gambia	Africa	54	91	38	31	45	35	2,050	1.4
Georgia	Asia/ME	74	24	100	99	100	73	2,560	5.1
Germany	Europe	78	4	–	–	–	88	25,350	82.4
Ghana	Africa	58	57	73	65	81	31	2,250	20.5
Greece	Europe	78	5	97	96	99	87	17,440	11.0
Guatemala	Lat/Car	66	36	69	62	77	26	4,400	12.0
Guinea	Africa	49	109	41	27	55	12	1,960	8.4
Guinea-Bissau	Africa	45	130	40	25	55	–	970	1.5
Guyana	Lat/Car	63	54	99	98	99	–	4,690	0.8
Haiti	Lat/Car	49	79	51	50	53	–	1,860	8.2
Honduras	Lat/Car	69	32	76	76	75	–	2,830	6.8
Hungary	Europe	72	8	99	99	100	87	12,340	9.9
Iceland	Europe	80	3	–	–	–	83	29,990	0.3
India	Asia/ME	64	67	58	46	69	–	2,840	1,049.5
Indonesia	Asia/ME	67	33	88	83	92	48	2,940	217.1
Iran	Asia/ME	70	35	77	70	84	–	6,000	68.1
Iraq	Asia/ME	60	102	40	23	55	–	*2,400	24.5
Ireland	Europe	77	6	–	–	–	–	32,410	3.9
Israel	Asia/ME	79	6	95	93	97	88	19,790	6.3
Italy	Europe	79	4	99	98	99	91	24,670	57.5
Jamaica	Lat/Car	76	17	87	91	83	74	3,720	2.6
Japan	Asia/ME	81	3	–	–	–	101	25,130	127.5
Jordan	Asia/ME	71	27	90	85	92	76	3,870	5.3
Kazakstan	Asia/ME	66	61	99	99	100	83	6,500	15.5
Kenya	Africa	45	78	83	77	90	23	980	31.5
Korea (Dem Rep of)	Asia/ME	63	42	98	99	96	–	*1,000	22.5
Korea (Rep of)	Asia/ME	75	5	98	97	99	91	15,090	47.4
Kuwait	Asia/ME	76	9	82	80	84	50	18,700	2.4
Kyrgyzstan	Asia/ME	68	52	97	–	–	–	2,750	5.1
Laos	Asia/ME	54	87	66	54	77	30	1,620	5.5
Latvia	Europe	71	17	100	100	100	74	7,730	2.3
Lebanon	Asia/ME	73	28	87	81	92	70	4,170	3.6

Sources: UNICEF, State of the World's Children 2004 and UNDP, Human Development Report 2003. *Estimates from CIA World Factbook

Country	Region	Life expectancy (2002)	Infant mortality per 1,000 births (2002)	Adult literacy (%) (2001)	Female adult literacy (2001 or latest available)	Male adult literacy (2001 or latest available)	Secondary school enrolment (2001)	GDP per capita in US dollars (2001) at purchasing power parity	Population in millions (2002)
Lesotho	Africa	36	64	84	94	73	21	2,420	1.8
Liberia	Africa	41	157	55	37	70	–	*1,000	3.2
Libya	Africa	73	16	81	70	91	–	7,570	5.4
Lithuania	Europe	73	8	100	100	100	89	8,470	3.4
Luxembourg	Europe	78	5	–	–	–		53,780	0.4
Macedonia	Europe	74	22	94	94	97	81	6,110	2.0
Madagascar	Africa	53	84	68	61	74	11	830	16.9
Malawi	Africa	38	114	61	48	75	25	570	11.9
Malaysia	Asia/ME	73	8	88	84	92	70	8,750	24.0
Maldives	Asia/ME	67	58	97	97	97	31	4,798	0.3
Mali	Africa	49	122	26	17	37	5	810	12.6
Malta	Europe	78	5	92	93	92	79	13,160	0.4
Mauritania	Africa	52	120	41	31	51	14	1,990	2.8
Mauritius	Africa	72	17	85	82	88	64	9,860	1.2
Mexico	Lat/Car	73	24	91	90	94	60	8,430	102.0
Micronesia	Oceania	68	20	67	67	66	–	*2,000	0.1
Moldova	Europe	69	27	99	98	100	68	2,150	4.3
Mongolia	Asia/ME	64	58	99	98	99	58	1,740	2.6
Morocco	Africa	68	39	50	37	63	30	3,600	30.1
Mozambique	Africa	38	125	45	30	61	9	1,140	18.5
Myanmar	Asia/ME	57	77	85	81	89	37	1,027	48.9
Namibia	Africa	45	55	83	82	83	38	7,120	2.0
Nepal	Asia/ME	60	66	43	25	61	–	1,310	24.6
Netherlands	Europe	78	5	–	–	–	90	27,190	16.1
New Zealand	Oceania	78	6	–	–	–	92	19,160	3.8
Nicaragua	Lat/Car	69	32	67	67	67	36	2,450	5.3
Niger	Africa	46	156	17	9	24	5	890	11.6
Nigeria	Africa	52	110	65	58	73	–	850	120.9
Norway	Europe	79	4	–	–	–	95	29,620	4.5
Oman	Asia/ME	72	11	73	64	81	59	12,040	2.8
Pakistan	Asia/ME	61	83	44	29	58	–	1,890	149.9
Palestinian OT	Asia/ME	72	23	89	–	–	78	–	3.4
Panama	Lat/Car	75	19	92	91	93	62	5,750	3.1
Papua New Guinea	Oceania	57	70	65	58	71	21	2,570	5.6
Paraguay	Lat/Car	71	26	94	93	95	47	5,210	5.7
Peru	Lat/Car	70	30	92	86	95	61	4,570	26.8
Philippines	Asia/ME	70	29	95	95	95	53	3,840	78.6
Poland	Europe	74	8	100	100	100	91	9,450	38.6
Portugal	Europe	76	5	93	90	95	85	18,150	10.0
Qatar	Asia/ME	72	11	82	84	81	78	19.844	0.6
Romania	Europe	71	19	98	97	99	80	5,830	22.4
Russia	Europe	67	18	100	99	100	–	7,100	144.1
Rwanda	Africa	39	96	68	62	75	–	1,250	8.3
St Lucia	Lat/Car	72	17	90	–	–	80	5,260	0.1
St Vincent & the Grenadines	Lat/Car	74	22	90	–	–	–	5,330	0.1

*Sources: UNICEF, State of the World's Children 2004 and UNDP, Human Development Report 2003. *Estimates from CIA World Factbook*

Country	Region	Life expectancy (2002)	Infant mortality per 1,000 births (2002)	Adult literacy (%) (2001)	Female adult literacy (2001 or latest available)	Male adult literacy (2001 or latest available)	Secondary school enrolment (2001)	GDP per capita in US dollars (2001) at purchasing power parity	Population in millions (2002)
Samoa	Oceania	70	20	99	98	99	68	6,180	0.2
Sao Tome & Principe	Africa	70	75	83	–	–	–	1,317	0.2
Saudi Arabia	Asia/ME	72	23	77	68	84	51	13,330	23.5
Senegal	Africa	53	79	38	29	48	–	1,500	9.9
Serbia & Montenegro	Europe	73	16	98	97	99	–	*2,200	10.5
Sierra Leone	Africa	34	165	36	23	51	26	470	4.8
Singapore	Asia/ME	78	3	93	89	96	–	22,680	4.2
Slovakia	Europe	74	8	100	100	100	75	11,960	5.4
Slovenia	Europe	76	4	100	100	100	–	17,130	2.0
Solomon Islands	Oceania	69	20	77	–	–	–	1,910	0.5
Somalia	Africa	48	133	24	–	–	–	*600	9.5
South Africa	Africa	49	52	86	85	86	57	11,290	44.8
Spain	Europe	79	4	98	97	99	94	20,150	41.0
Sri Lanka	Asia/ME	73	17	92	89	95	–	3,180	18.9
Sudan	Africa	56	64	59	48	70	–	1,970	32.9
Suriname	Lat/Car	71	31	94	93	96	43	4,599	0.4
Swaziland	Africa	36	106	80	79	81	44	4,330	1.1
Sweden	Europe	80	3	–	–	–	96	24,180	8.9
Switzerland	Europe	79	5	–	–	–	88	28,100	7.2
Syria	Asia/ME	72	23	75	62	89	39	3,280	17.4
Tajikistan	Asia/ME	69	53	99	99	100	76	1,170	6.2
Tanzania	Africa	44	104	76	68	85	5	520	36.3
Thailand	Asia/ME	69	24	96	94	97	–	6,400	62.2
Timor-Leste	Asia/ME	49	89	–	–	–	–	*500	0.7
Togo	Africa	50	79	58	44	73	23	1,650	4.8
Tonga	Oceania	68	16	99	–	–	–	*2,200	0.1
Trinidad and Tobago	Lat/Car	71	17	98	98	99	71	9,100	1.3
Tunisia	Africa	73	21	72	62	82	70	6,390	9.7
Turkey	Asia/ME	70	36	86	77	94	–	5,890	70.3
Turkmenistan	Asia/ME	67	76	98	–	–	–	4,320	4.8
Uganda	Africa	46	82	68	58	78	12	1,490	25.0
Ukraine	Europe	70	16	100	100	100	–	4,350	48.9
United Arab Emirates	Asia/ME	75	8	77	80	75	67	20,530	2.9
United Kingdom	Europe	78	5	–	–	–	94	24,160	59.1
United States	N.Amer	77	7	–	–	–	88	34,320	291.0
Uruguay	Lat/Car	75	14	98	98	97	70	8,400	3.4
Uzbekistan	Asia/ME	70	52	99	99	100	–	2,460	25.7
Vanuatu	Oceania	69	34	34	–	–	23	3,190	0.2
Venezuela	Lat/Car	74	19	93	92	93	50	5,670	25.2
Viet Nam	Asia/ME	69	30	93	91	95	62	2,070	80.3
Yemen	Asia/ME	60	79	48	27	69	37	790	19.3
Zambia	Africa	33	108	79	73	86	19	780	10.7
Zimbabwe	Africa	34	76	89	86	93	40	2,280	12.8

*Sources: UNICEF, State of the World's Children 2004 and UNDP, Human Development Report 2003. *Estimates from CIA World Factbook*

Appendix 2:

The Universal Declaration of Human Rights 1948

(Simplified version by Amnesty International UK)

Article 1
We are all born free and equal. We all have our own thoughts and ideas. We shall all be treated in the same way. We shall treat each other with respect.

Article 2
These rights belong to everybody, whatever our differences.

Article 3
We all have the right to life, and to live in freedom and safety.

Article 4
Nobody has any right to make us a slave and we cannot make anyone else our slave.

Article 5
Nobody has the right to hurt us or to torture us.

Article 6
We all have the same right to use the law.

Article 7
The law is the same for everyone. It must treat us all fairly.

Article 8
We can all ask for the law to help us when we are not fairly treated and to give us a remedy.

Article 9
Nobody has the right to put us in prison without good reason, to keep us there or to send us away from our country.

Article 10
If we are put on trial, this should be in public. The people who try us should not let anyone tell them what to do.

Article 11
Nobody should be blamed for doing something until it is proved. When people say we did a bad thing we have the right to show that it is untrue.

Article 12
Nobody should try to harm our good name. Nobody has the right to come into our home, open our letters, or bother us or our family without good reason.

Article 13
We all have the right to go wherever we want in our own country and travel abroad if we wish.

Article 14
If we are frightened or badly treated in our own country, we all have the right to emigrate to another country for our own safety.

Article 15
We all have the right to citizenship of a country.

The Universal Declaration of Human Rights 1948 (cont)

(Simplified version by Amnesty International UK)

Article 16
Every adult has the right to marry and have a family if they wish. Men and women have the same rights when they are married as well as before, during and after marriage.

Article 17
Everyone has the right to own things or share them. Nobody should take our possessions from us without a good reason.

Article 18
We all have the right to believe in whatever we wish, to have a faith and to change this if we wish.

Article 19
We all have the right to make up our own minds, to think what we like, and say what we think, as well as to share our ideas with other people.

Article 20
We all have the right to meet our friends and to work together in peace to defend our rights. Nobody can make us join a group if we don't want to.

Article 21
We all have the right to take part in the government of our country. All adults should be allowed to choose the leaders of their country and their representatives.

Article 22
We all have the right to a home, enough money to live on, and medical help if we are ill. Music, art and craft, and sport should be for everyone to enjoy.

Article 23
Every adult has the right to a job, to a fair wage for their work and to join a trade union and choose what work they do.

Article 24
We all have the right to rest from our work, to relax and have holidays.

Article 25
We all have the right to enjoy a good life. Mothers, children, the elderly, the unemployed and the disabled have the right to be cared for.

Article 26
Education is a right, and primary school should be free. We should learn about the UN and how to co-operate with others. Our parents may choose our education.

Article 27
We all have the right to our own way of life, and to enjoy the good things that science and learning can bring. We all can enjoy rewards from literature and artistic work.

Article 28
There must be political order and stability so that we can all enjoy rights and freedom not only in our own country but worldwide.

Article 29
We all have a duty to other people and we should protect their rights and freedom.

Article 30
Nobody can take away these rights and freedoms from us.

Appendix 3: Recommended resources

Useful reading

Banners and Dragons: the complete guide to creative campaigning, Jones, Dan. Amnesty International, 2003

Comparative Electoral Systems, Newland, Robert. Electoral Reform Society,1982

The Crystal Maze, Dodd, Philip. 2000. Available from Philip Dodd, 73 Beech Grove, Whitley Bay, Tyne & Wear, NE26 3PL.

Fact File, updated annually. Carel Press (www.carelpress.com).

Freedom! Human Rights Education Pack, Adams, Caroline, Harrow, Marietta and Jones, Dan. Amnesty International and Hodder and Stoughton, 2001.

Global Mathematics: A Second Multicultural Resource Book, Dodd, Philip. 1993. (Available from Philip Dodd, 73 Beech Grove, Whitley Bay, Tyne & Wear, NE26 3PL.)

Human Rights in the Curriculum: French, Ed. Brown, Margot. Amnesty International, 2002.

Human Rights in the Curriculum: History, Ed Brown, Margot and Slater, Sara. Amnesty International, 2002.

Human Rights in the Curriculum: Spanish, Ed Brown, Margot. Amnesty International, 2002.

Learning about human rights through Citizenship. Amnesty International, 2001. (Product code YA278. Free from Amnesty International UK, PO Box 4, Rugby, Warwickshire CV21 1RU telephone 01788 545553.)

Mathematics from Around the World: A Multicultural Resource Book, Dodd, Philip. 1989. (Available from Philip Dodd, 73 Beech Grove, Whitley Bay, Tyne & Wear, NE26 3PL.)

Mathematics from China, Straker, Anita. ESM, 1990. (ESM, Duke Street, Wisbech, Cambs, PE13 2AE.)

Multicultural Mathematics Resources, Smile Mathematics (www.smilemathematics.co.uk)

Multiple Factors: Classroom Mathematics for Equality and Justice, Shan, Sharan-Jeet and Bailey, Peter. Trentham Books, 1991. (Trentham Books, Westview House, 734 London Road, Oakhill, Stoke-on Trent ST4 5NP.)

New Internationalist magazine, New Internationalist (www.newint.org)

Peters Projection map of the world, New Internationalist (www.newint.org)

Rights of the Child A1 poster and A4 teaching notes. Amnesty International, 2003. (Product codeYA725. Free from Amnesty International UK, PO Box 4, Rugby, Warwickshire CV21 1RU telephone 01788 545553.)

Spilling the Beans on the Coffee Trade, Fairtrade Foundation, 2002. (www.fairtrade.org.uk)

Summing up the World: Mathematical Activities with a Global Perspective. DEED, 1993. (DEED, Kingsleigh School, Hadow Road, Bournemouth, BH10 5HS.)

The World Guide, Instituto del Tercer Mundo. Biennial. Available from New Internationalist (www.newint.org)

Useful human rights websites

Electoral Reform Society	www.electoral-reform.org.uk
Equal Opportunities Commission	www.eoc.org.uk
Fairtrade Foundation	www.fairtrade.org.uk
Global Express	www.dep.org.uk/globalexpress
Inter-Parliamentary Union	www.ipu.org
New Internationalist	www.newint.org
Refugee Council	www.refugeecouncil.org.uk
United Nations Children's Fund	www.unicef.org
United Nations Development Programme	www.undp.org
United Nations Educational, Scientific & Cultural Org - Institute of Statistics	www.uis.unesco.org
United Nations High Commission for Refugees	www.unhcr.ch
United Nations Population Fund	www.unfpa.org
WaterAid	www.wateraid.org.uk
Water UK	www.water.org.uk

Index

References to "Teacher's notes" pages are indicated with a *tn* suffix in the index below